DATE DUE			

HIGH MODULUS
FIBERS AND COMPOSITES

FRANCIS S. GALASSO

United Aircraft Research Laboratories

GORDON AND BREACH, SCIENCE PUBLISHERS
New York / London / Paris

Copyright © 1969 by GORDON AND BREACH, Science Publishers, Inc.
150 Fifth Avenue, New York, N.Y. 10011

Library of Congress Catalog Card Number: 71-104394

Editorial office for Great Britain:
Gordon and Breach, Science Publishers Ltd.
12 Bloomsbury Way
London W.C. 1

Editorial office for France:
Gordon & Breach
7-9 rue Emile Dubois
Paris 14e

Printed in the United States of America

PREFACE

The continuous demands for improved materials for structural applications have provided the impetus for the rapid advances in fiber and composite technology. Of particular interest in the past few years have been the high modulus fibers and composites developed for use in lightweight, stiff structures for space age applications. Some of these fibers such as boron and carbon fibers are suitable for use in epoxy resin composites, while other fibers such as silicon carbide and silicon carbide coated boron fibers were prepared for use in metals for elevated temperature applications.

The available information on high modulus fibers and composites is becoming of greater interest as the number of applications for these materials increase. This book was written to provide this information for fiber researchers, composite workers and those interested in the most advanced structural materials. It is meant to be an introduction to this rapidly growing field. Some data are provided on glass and metal fibers, but the main emphasis has been placed on high modulus continuous fibers and epoxy resin and metal matrix composites which contain these fibers.

In addition to the "man made" composites formed by introducing fibers in a matrix material, "natural" or eutectic composites are also covered. These composites are prepared by unidirectionally solidifying eutectic systems so as to produce a controlled microstructure. Since the microstructures are stable at elevated temperatures, it is expected that these materials will be particularly suitable for use at these temperatures.

This book presents the state of the art in the spring of 1969 and covers the work conducted on high modulus fibers and composites which began in the early 1960's. The author has chosen information which he felt would be valuable to researchers and students who wish a concise review of this field.

The preparation of this book was facilitated by the assistance of Professor R. Smoluchowski and Dr. R. Graf who read the manuscript. I am grateful to Dr. R. Pike and Dr. K. Kreider for information on composites, to Mr. J. Hermann for optical photomicrographs, and Mr. W. Tice for electron micrographs and electron diffraction photographs. I am also indebted to Mrs. J. Pinto, Mrs. L. Jenkins, and my wife, Lois, for assistance in the preparation of the manuscript.

CONTENTS

Chapter 5

COMPOSITES

FIBERS AND COMPOSITES

INTRODUCTION

GENERAL FEATURES OF FIBERS AND COMPOSITES

The rapid advances in high modulus composite materials have been made possible by the recent emergence of new and improved fibers. A list of fibers and their properties is given in Table 1.1. These fibers can be united with plastics and metals in various configurations to obtain properties superior to those attainable with either component alone. Because this type of composite is produced by physically combining the fibers and matrices they are sometimes referred to as "man made" composites. This is in contrast to the unidirectional solidification of eutectics which produces aligned reinforcement elements in a matrix in a single operation.[1] Since both components are formed during solidification from solution, this type of composite is sometimes called a "natural" composite. In this introduction various fibers are discussed in terms of their potential for use in lightweight high modulus composites.

GLASS FIBERS

One of the most successful "man made" composites is the glass reinforced resin composite which has been used extensively in the past twenty years for both military and civilian applications. Glass fibers have reached their present state of popularity because of their relatively low cost and high tensile strength, which is over 500,000 psi, in the virgin state. The reason commercial glass fibers are inexpensive is that they can be drawn in large numbers at rates of greater than 1000 ft/min from a

FIBERS AND COMPOSITES

Table 1.1

DATA FOR FIBERS

Filaments	Diameter (mils)	Density		UTS (10^3 psi)	Specific UTS (10^6 in.)	Modulus (10^6 psi)	Specific Modulus (10^6 in.)
		(g/cm³)	(lbs/in.³)				
SiO_2	1.4	2.2	0.078	850	10.8	10	133
E-glass	0.4	2.6	0.092	500	5.4	12	130
S-glass	0.4	2.5	0.090	650	7.2	13	140
M-glass	---	2.9	0.103	500	4.7	16	155
Al	6.0	2.7	0.092	13	0.1	10	109
Nb	6.0	8.6	0.308	50	0.2	15	49
Ta	6.0	16.8	0.594	48	0.1	27	45
Ti	6.0	4.5	0.161	78	0.5	17	106
Fe_{ss}	6.0	7.9	0.282	347	1.2	30	106
W	6.0	19.3	0.690	420	0.6	50	73
B/W	4.0	2.6	0.092	450	4.9	55	600
C_T	0.3	1.6	0.057	285	5.0	50	880
C_M	0.3	1.9	0.068	250	3.7	60	880
SiC/B/W	4.3	2.8	0.100	430	4.3	55	550
SiC/W	4.0	3.5	0.125	300	2.4	65	520

Al$_2$O$_3$	9.0	4.0	0.143	380	2.7	40	280
BN	0.3	1.9	0.068	200	2.9	13	188
ZrO$_2$	--	4.9	0.175	300	1.7	50	286
TiB$_2$/W	--	--	--	150	--	70	--
B$_4$C/W	2.5	2.7	0.095	390	4.1	62	650
Be	5.0	1.8	0.066	185	2.8	35	530
Whiskers							
Al$_2$O$_3$	< 0.1-0.3	4.0	0.143	1000	7.0	70	489
SiC	0.1	3.2	0.114	3000	26.1	70	608
Si$_3$N$_4$	≤ 0.1-0.4	3.2	0.114	700	6.1	40	350

C_T - Thornel carbon fiber

C_M - Morganite carbon fiber

single platinum bushing. While degradation of these fibers due to rubbing
and atmospheric impurities is a problem, it is minimized by coating the
individual fibers with a sizing.

In spite of its excellent strength, pure SiO_2 fiber cannot be used
for many Space Age applications because of its low modulus ($\sim 10 \times 10^6$ psi).
As a consequence, a great deal of work has been conducted recently to improve the modulus of glass. One of the approaches for obtaining high modulus glasses has involved modification of glass compositions. Commercial
"E" glass, for example, contains about 14% Al_2O_3, 18% CaO, 5% MgO, 8% B_2O_3
and 1% Na_2O + K_2O as well as silica. The modulus of this glass is approximately 12×10^6 psi.[2,3] "S" glass is still higher modulus glass. It contains about 25% Al_2O_3 and 10% MgO with SiO_2. When this glass fiber is
thermally compacted it has a modulus of 13×10^6 psi.

By inclusion of BeO in glasses the modulus has been increased still
further.[4] Workers at the National Bureau of Standards developed one of
these glasses called "M" glass. In subsequent experiments, Owens-Corning
Fiberglas investigated the feasibility of fiberizing the National Bureau
of Standard's glass under Air Force Sponsorship, and found that the composition had to be modified before the glass could be drawn.[5] The glass
that they ended up producing as fibers contained 53.7% SiO_2, 12.9% CaO,
9.0% MgO, 8.0% BeO, 7.9% TiO_2, 3.0% CeO_2, 3.0% Li_2O, 2.0% ZrO_2, and 0.50%
Fe_2O_3. The modulus of this fiber was found to be 15.9×10^6 psi and the
density $2.89 g/cm^3$.

Aerojet-General Corporation also has achieved a modulus in the
16×10^6 psi range for a glass containing BeO, and Bacon of United Aircraft Research Laboratories, under NASA sponsorship, has drawn fibers with
similar moduli from glasses which do not contain BeO. This latter achieve-
ment is significant because the toxicity of BeO has caused some concern
as to the acceptance of glasses which have BeO as one of its constituents.

Fig. 1.1. Beryllium-glass hand drawn specimen, Magnification 139X.

METAL FIBERS

In order to find higher modulus fibers, one has to look to metal and crystalline ceramic fibers. Most of these metals can be prepared in a fine wire form by drawing large diameter wires through a series of diamond dies. The main expense in preparing fibers in this manner is the large capital investment for the dies and for equipment time required to reduce the wire diameter.

Attempts have been made to reduce the cost of metal fibers by developing new techniques for their formation. In one study, Cox et al[6], under Navy Sponsorship demonstrated that short lengths of beryllium fibers could be hand drawn in a glass envelope (See Fig. 1.1). They conducted additional investigations, using a continuous process based on the principle first used by Taylor[7] in which a metal is cast in a glass container as the

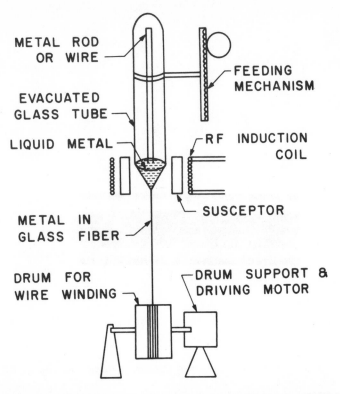

METAL ROD
OR WIRE

FEEDING
MECHANISM

EVACUATED
GLASS TUBE

LIQUID METAL

RF INDUCTION
COIL

METAL IN
GLASS FIBER

SUSCEPTOR

DRUM FOR
WIRE WINDING

DRUM SUPPORT &
DRIVING MOTOR

Fig. 1.2. Schematic of composite metal fiber processing technique.

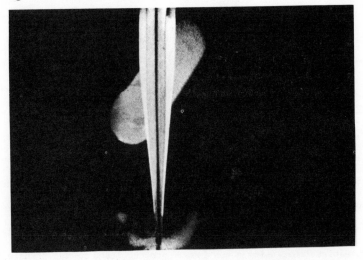

Fig. 1.3. Copper fiber being drawn in glass.

glass is drawn into a fiber. A schematic of this process is shown in
Fig. 1.2. In the continuous process, reaction between beryllium and glass
proved to be a problem. Some success, however, was obtained in drawing
chromium, iron, aluminum, and various ceramic fibers in limited studies on
these systems.

A thorough evaluation of this technique was made using copper as a
model system. Several thousand feet of copper in glass fibers were drawn
continuously from a two-foot long specimen of glass tubing containing
copper. A photograph of copper fiber being formed is shown in Fig. 1.3.
When the fibers were drawn at a speed of approximately 230 ft/min, continuous lengths of 15 mil diameter copper fibers up to 50 feet long were
obtained. At drawing rates of 2600 ft/min, fibers with copper core diameters of less than a micron were formed. However, the cores of these
latter fibers were not continuous.

These studies showed that a number of materials could be drawn by
selecting glasses having softening temperatures and melting temperatures
which bracket the melting point of the material to be fiberized. In addition, there were indications that small streams of molten metal squirted
into the fiber-forming zone of glass during the drawing process would mini-
mize the glass-metal reaction. Thus, reactive metals might be formed as
fibers by this process. Removal of the fibers was achieved in many cases
by dissolving the glass with hydrofluoric acid.

In other studies, Pond[8] conducted experiments in which liquid metals
were squirted from a small orifice. In a modified technique, Monsanto
demonstrated that short lengths of boron fiber could be squirted if the
stream was stabilized by a BN coating. To date, these fibers have not had
the strengths comparable to those produced by pyrolytic techniques.

Schile[9] developed equipment for squirting high temperature materials
into a chamber in which the atmosphere could be controlled. In some

initial experiments, Al-CuAl$_2$ and Al-Al$_3$Ni eutectics were squirted by
applying a pressure of 25 psi of helium on the melts contained in a boron
nitride crucible. The liquid jets were stabilized by squirting them into
still air with additional air being injected below the crucible. The aluminum oxide formed on the surface of these molten streams appeared to
stabilize them. The Al-CuAl$_2$ eutectic alloy solidified with a nebulous
pattern of these two phases, while the Al-Al$_3$Ni eutectic alloy, after
squirting, contained Al and a mixture of aluminum-nickel phases.

Recently Brunswick Corporation developed a method for drawing many
metal wires together through an orifice with oxides to produce fine metal
filaments. A number of these metal fibers such as nickel base superalloys,
tantalum and stainless steel are now sold commercially. They are essential-
ly circular in cross section and the diameters are in the 4 to 50 micron
range.

Achievements such as these have helped to create interest in metal
fibers for reinforcing materials. However, there are many space age applications for which metal fibers are not suitable. While the main problem
with glasses in these cases is their low moduli, the main deterent to using
high modulus metals is their high densities.

Niobium and titanium wires have moduli slightly higher than "M" glass,
15.2 and 16.8 x 10^6 psi respectively. However, the density of niobium is
8.6 g/cm^3 and even the density of titanium, 4.5 g/cm^3, is high in comparison to the density of "M" glass. Iron and nickel fibers with a modulus of
30 x 10^6 psi and tungsten fiber with a modulus of 50 x 10^6 psi are much
stiffer than glass fibers. Many studies have demonstrated the value of
employing stainless steel and tungsten wires as reinforcement in composites,
but the density of steel (7.9 g/cm^3) and tungsten (19.3 g/cm^3) is much
higher than is desired for many special aerospace applications.

WHISKERS

Because of the limitations of glass and metal fibers previously described, materials scientists desiring both lower density and higher modulus
fiber have had to look to more exotic materials. There are a number of
these high modulus materials which have been prepared as whiskers. Of
these, only sapphire, silicon carbide and silicon nitride whiskers are
available in quantity.

Mertz[10] reported the preparation of silicon carbide whiskers by the
pyrolysis of organosilanes such as methyltrichlorosilane in hydrogen at
temperatures from 1500° to 2000°C. In other studies, Iley and Riley[11,12]
obtained silicon carbide whiskers by the pyrolysis of wet ethylene in silica
tubes at 1300°C and Alley et al[13] prepared silicon carbide whiskers by the
reduction of silicates with carbon at temperatures from 1350 to 1700°C.

Carborundum prepares silicon carbide whiskers with a density of
3.17 g/cm^3, a length of 100 to 750 microns, a diameter of 1 to 3 microns,
a strength of 3×10^6 psi and a modulus of 70×10^6 psi.

Silicon nitride whiskers are prepared by a vapor phase reaction between silicon and a silicate in nitrogen and hydrogen at a temperature of
$1400°C$. The density of the whiskers is 0.115 lbs/in.^{3}, the diameters are
from 1 to 10 microns, the strength is greater than 700×10^3 psi and the
elastic modulus is 40×10^6 psi.

The most thoroughly studied whiskers are those of alumina. They are
produced by passing a stream of moist hydrogen over aluminum powder heated
to 1300-1500°C. The strength of these whiskers is typically 1×10^6 psi
and the modulus is 70×10^6 psi, but Soltis[14] showed that the elastic
modulus parallel to the a-axis $\langle 10 \bar{1} 0 \rangle$ can have values of 222 to
230×10^6 psi, perpendicular to the a-axis $\langle 11 \bar{2} 0 \rangle$ from 90 to 180×10^6
psi and parallel to the c-axis from 27 to 71×10^6 psi.

Other whiskers also have been produced in smaller quantities. Beryllium oxide whiskers have been grown using water vapor to volatilize beryllium oxide,[15] magnesium oxide whiskers have been prepared by the reduction
of magnesium oxide with hydrogen, carbon or tungsten,[16] tungsten oxide
whiskers have been formed by reacting tungsten and magnesium oxide,[17] and
carbon whiskers have been grown by sublimation in a dc-arc between graphite
electrodes.[18]

Whiskers have been studied extensively because they represent a nearly
perfect structural form of a material as evidenced by their high strengths.
The theoretical value for perfect whiskers is about one tenth of the elastic modulus, but the actual values are of the order of 1×10^6 psi. In
spite of this strength, whiskers have not found wide usage because of their
high costs and the difficulty in aligning them in a matrix. Because of the
immediate requirements for better materials, aerospace materials designers
and fabricators have favored continuous fibers for use in composite structures causing a large growth in the interest and activity on high modulus
filaments of materials such as boron, carbon, and silicon carbide.

HIGH MODULUS FILAMENTS

Boron, carbon and similar filaments could not be prepared by conventional techniques commonly used in the formation of glass and metal fibers,
and, as a consequence, elaborate methods had to be developed to form this
type of fiber. Because of the complexity of some of these techniques the
cost of the fibers was quite high initially. Boron fiber, for example,
in the development-stages in 1965, cost approximately $7000/lb. However,
the high strength and modulus of boron fiber along with its low density
created a great deal of interest in this fiber for applications where
weight savings were extremely important. In the next few years, the cost
dropped to below $300/lb and the average tensile strength of the fiber

increased from 300,000 psi to 450,000 psi as the fiber moved from the development stage into production. It is anticipated that the cost will
decrease and the strength will increase still further in the near future.

Carbon fiber technology also has had a remarkable rate of growth.
This fiber in tow form was being developed in England and in yarn form at
Union Carbide in the United States during the same period boron fiber de-
velopment was progressing at a number of companies in the United States.
In England the carbon fiber tow was produced by pyrolyzing and graphitiz-
ing polyacrylonitrile precursor fiber, while Union Carbide employed rayon
in their process. In both processes, the objective was to align the graphite layers in the fiber to increase the modulus. The progression of the
Union Carbide fibers was easy to follow as they marketed the Thornel series
T-25, then T-40 and later T-50, where the number designates the modulus of
the fiber in msi. Morganite and Courtaulds of England also produced a
series of carbon fibers with increasing moduli, but they still sell the
lower modulus fibers because the low modulus fibers have higher strengths
than the higher modulus ones.

The main attributes of carbon fiber are the low density, which is
1.9 g/cm^3 for fibers produced from polyacrylonitrile and 1.6 g/cm^3 for
fibers formed from rayon, the potentially very high modulus, and the flexi-
bility of the very fine fibers in the yarn. The undesirable features of
carbon fiber are the variability in its strength and modulus and the low
shear strength of composites made using the carbon fiber as reinforcement,
which is lower for higher modulus fibers. However, in recent years the
shear strength of carbon-epoxy composites has been improved by treating
the surface of the fibers. These treated fibers can now be obtained from
most of the companies which sell carbon fibers.

For high temperature applications in metal matrices, silicon carbide
coated boron fiber manufactured by Hamilton Standard Division of United

Aircraft and sold under the trade name BORSIC® is far superior to uncoated
boron fiber. The strength and modulus of silicon carbide coated boron
fiber are comparable to those of boron, and the oxidation resistance is
much better.[19] In addition, the silicon carbide coating prevents the
boron from reacting with the metals used as the matrices. It is estimated
that the price of silicon carbide coated boron fiber eventually will be
about the same as that of uncoated boron fiber.

Silicon carbide fiber is also a high temperature fiber with good
oxidation resistant properties. The main reason it has not become as
widely used in composites as boron fiber is that it has a lower strength
($\sim$ 300,000 psi) and costs a great deal more to produce.[20] However, the
amount of research on this fiber has not been sufficient to fully evaluate
or develop it.

Other fibers listed in Table 1.1 are still in various stages of
development. Aluminum oxide fibers have been produced in polycrystalline
form by extruding alumina powder in an organic matrix and burning off the
organic material and recently, single crystal sapphire fiber has been prepared by drawing it from a melt. Its strength of 380,000 psi and modulus
of 40×10^6 psi along with its inertness makes it an attractive candidate
for high temperature metal matrix composites. Only its relatively high
density of 4 g/cm^3 and the difficulty in bonding it to metals causes concern to composite researchers and developers.

Boron nitride fiber also has been used in composite studies because
of resistance to attack by metals. In spite of its inertness and low
density, boron nitride fiber has not been used to a greater extent due to
its low modulus.

Zirconium dioxide, TiB_2 and B_4C are other experimental high temperature fibers being considered for use in composites. Zirconium dioxide
has been produced by extrusion of the powder in an organic binder, and

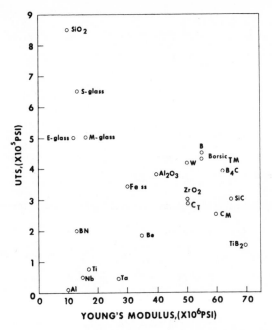

Fig. 1.4. UTS versus Young's modulus for filaments (C_M-Morganite carbon fiber, C_T-Union Carbide carbon fiber).

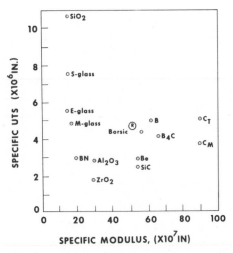

Fig. 1.5. Specific UTS versus specific modulus for filaments(C_M-Morganite carbon fiber, C_T-Union Carbide carbon fiber).

TiB_2 and B_4C have been formed by chemical vapor deposition techniques. Not enough work has been conducted on these fibers to determine their full potential.

Beryllium fibers are also of interest because they have both a low density and a high modulus. However, unlike many of the other metals, beryllium is difficult to produce as a fine fiber by drawing down large diameter wires. Some fiber has been produced by drawing the metal in a glass envelope,[6] but unless this or another novel technique can be successfully employed for forming beryllium fiber, it will remain too expensive to use for most of the projected applications of composite materials.

Of the glass metal and crystalline inorganic fibers described in the introduction, the high modulus filaments (long and continuous fibers) discussed in this last section are the most practical for use in lightweight composites at the present time. As a consequence, they were chosen as the topics to be covered in more detail in the next chapters. Emphasis has been placed on boron, silicon carbide coated boron and carbon fibers. As can be seen in Fig. 1.4 and 1.5, on a strength and modulus basis, boron and Borsic filaments are outstanding and on a specific strength and specific modulus basis, carbon filaments also must be included with the other two filaments. In the last chapter, plastic and metal matrix composites containing these filaments are discussed as well as unidirectionally solidified eutectic composites.

REFERENCES

1. M. J. Salkind, F. D. George, F. D. Lemkey, B. J. Bayles, and J. A. Ford, Chem. Eng. Progress, 62, 52 (1966).

2. R. A. Schoenlaub, U. S. Patent No. 2, 334, 961 (1943).

3. R. L. Tiede and F. V. Tooley, U. S. Patent No. 2, 571, 074 (1951).

4. G. R. Machlan, Owens-Corning Fiberglas Corp., WADD TR 55-290 (AD 80373) (1955).

5.   P. J. Frickert, R. L. Tiede, H. I. Glaser and A. B. Isham, WADD
     Technical Report 60-24, March (1960).

6.   J. Cox, R. Veltri and C. Shulze, AD 463, 903, March (1965).

7.   G. F. Taylor, Phys. Rev., 23, 655 (1924).

8.   R. Pond, U. S. Patent 2, 907, 082, October (1959).

9.   R. Schile, W. R. Lasko, F. S. Galasso et al, Technical Report
     AFML-TR-66-345 December (1966).

10. K. M. Merz, Silicon Carbide, Proc. Conf. Boston, April (1959).
     Ed. by J. R. O'Connor and J. Smiltens, Pergammon Press, New York
     (1960).

11. R. Iley and H. L. Riley, Nature, 160, 468 (1947).

12. R. Iley and H. L. Riley, Chem. Soc. Journal, 42, 274 (1948).

13. J. K. Alley, R. C. Johnson, C. Huggins, and H. R. Shell, U.S. Bureau
     of Mines, Ri-6220 (1963).

14. P. J. Soltis, U.S. Naval Air Eng. Rpt. No. NAEC-AML-1831 (1964).

15. S. B. Austerman, J. Am. Cer. Soc., 46, 1 (1963).

16. M. M. Butcher and E. A. D. White, J. Am. Cer. Soc. 48, 9, 492 (1965).

17. E. G. Wolff, J. Am. Cer. Soc., 48, 4, 221 (1965).

18. R. Bacon, J. Appl. Phys., 31, 2, 283 (1960).

19. M. Basche, R. Fanti and F. Galasso, Fibre Science and Technology,
     1, 19 (1968).

20. F. Galasso, M. Basche and D. Kuehl, Appl. Phys. Letters, 9, 37 (1966).

2

BORON FIBERS

INTRODUCTION

The preparation of continuous high modulus boron fibers represents one of the most significant developments in structural materials in the past decade. The first boron fibers were formed as early as 1911 by Weintraub who reduced boron halide with hydrogen on a hot wire substrate.[1] In the years that followed, boron was studied as a bulk structural material. However, it was not until 1960 when Talley used this process to prepare high strength "amorphous" boron fibers, that the interest in boron began to grow rapidly.[2] The United States Air Force quickly realized the potential of boron fiber as a reinforcement for lightweight aerospace composite structures and speeded its development by sponsoring and conducting research to improve the strength of this fiber and increase its rate of formation. In this research a number of schemes such as melt spinning, electrolysis and chemical vapor deposition were investigated as means of producing the fiber. Melt spinning resulted in low strength fiber and other techniques did not produce the same quality fiber as the chemical vapor deposition techniques which used diborane and boron trichloride as sources of boron. The diborane process looked attractive in initial studies because lower temperatures could be employed; thus substrates such as carbon coated glass and low melting metals could be considered as substrates for the process. In spite of this advantage, the higher temperature boron trichloride-hydrogen process was deemed the better one because its use resulted in fibers with greater uniformity in strength. For this

reason, in the late 1960's the Hamilton Standard Division of United Aircraft, Texaco, Avco and Wacker-Chemie GMBH (Munich) adopted this method
to produce continuous boron fiber commercially.

PREPARATION

In the BCl_3 process, fine tungsten wire is drawn through a mercury
atmospheric seal into a reaction chamber and out another mercury seal.
The mercury seals which act as electrical contacts to the wire permit the
wire to be resistively heated as boron trichloride and hydrogen gases
pass into the reactor, and react on the hot wire. The excess gases exit
with the by-product gases. Both Hamilton Standard and Avco employ 0.0005
in. diameter tungsten wire as a substrate while Wacker-Chemie uses 0.0004
in. diameter tungsten wire in the production of 0.004 in. diameter boron
fiber.

The reactors used to prepare the boron fibers vary from a single stage
reactor such as the one shown in Fig. 2.1 to complicated multistaged units.
Some boron reactors are operated vertically and others horizontally. While
configurations using multiple filaments have been considered, the most
successful to date, are the ones which produce a single boron filament in
each reactor.

The rate of boron deposition increases with faster gas flow rates
and the gas concentrations normally used are approximately those dictated
by the equation:

$$2 \; BCl_3 + 3 \; H_2 \longrightarrow 2 \; B + 6 \; HCl$$

The rate of boron deposition also increases with increasing wire
temperature. However, above 1250°C spurious growths form which produce
weak spots on the fiber. At higher temperatures $>$1400°C crystalline
boron is produced. The rate of growth of the crystalline boron fiber is

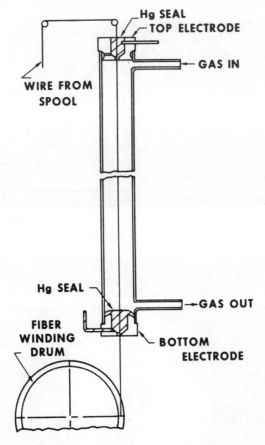

Fig. 2.1. Vertical boron reactor.

more rapid than that of amorphous boron but the average tensile strength of crystalline boron fiber is only ~ 200,000 psi as compared to 450,000 psi for amorphous boron fiber.

While 0.0005 in. diameter tungsten wire is used almost exclusively as the substrate in production, carbon, carbon coated glass,[3] metal coated glass fibers and iron, tantalum, columbium and molybdenum[4] wires also have been considered. Obtaining coated glass fibers with uniform electrical resistance has presented a major problem in using these types of materials, while undesirable reactions with boron or high cost has made

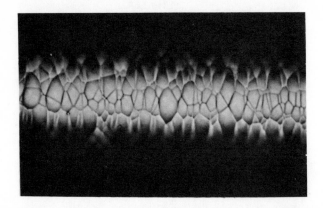

Fig. 2.2. Photomicrograph of surface of boron fiber.

Fig. 2.3. Photomicrograph of etched polished cross section of boron fiber.

the use of metal wires, other than tungsten wire, unsuitable.[5] It is
difficult for other metals to compete with tungsten as a substrate because
the strength of tungsten wire makes it particularly suitable for drawing
down into a very fine wire and for handling in a boron forming reactor.

MICROSTRUCTURE AND STRUCTURE

The surface of the boron fiber produced by the BCl_3-H_2 process con-
sists of nodules which are the culmination of cones grown from nucleation
sites at the surface of the substrate. See Fig. 2.2. Therefore, the size
of the nodules increases as the diameter of the fiber increases.

As the tungsten wire is drawn through the reactor, boron is continuously deposited. When multichambered reactors are employed, boundary
layers can be seen in magnified etched cross sections of the fiber produced
in these reactors. See Fig. 2.3. The cones continue to grow as the fiber
passes from one chamber through the mercury into the next chamber. However, if dirt particles are picked up in the seal, they act as new nucleation sites from which new cones grow and disrupt the structure, resulting
in weak points in the fiber. This points out the importance of keeping
the mercury in these seals clean.

X-ray studies on the boron fibers produced below 1300°C indicate
that the boron is amorphous. The X-ray pattern of the boron consisted of
four broad halos at d-spacings of 4.3, 2.5, 1.7 and 1.4Å. In spite of
the diffuse pattern, Gillespie still felt that the boron was really
crystalline,[6] and attributed the broad diffraction lines to fine grains.
Otte and Lipsitt[7] also felt the boron was crystalline but concluded that
the lines in the X-ray pattern were diffuse because the boron was highly
faulted. They reported that electron diffraction patterns of crushed
fragments showed the β-rhombohedral boron reflections and attributed the
diffuseness in the X-ray pattern to residual strains in the boron and
particle surface diffraction.

Fig. 2.4. Transmission electron micrograph of fragment of boron fiber (after Galasso et al[8]).

Fig. 2.5. Selected-area electron diffraction pattern of a fragment of boron fiber (after Galasso et al[8]).

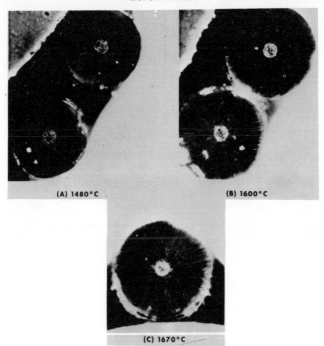

(A) 1480°C   (B) 1600°C

(C) 1670°C

Fig. 2.6. Polished cross sections of boron filaments formed at different temperatures a) 1480°C; b) 1600°C; c) 1670°C. Cross-polarized light. X500 (after Galasso et al[9]).

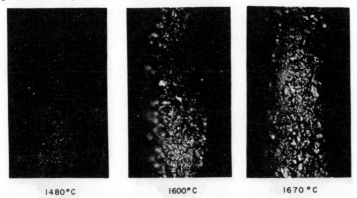

1480°C   1600°C   1670°C

Fig. 2.7. Photomicrographs of boron filament surfaces formed at different temperatures; a) 1480°C; b) 1600°C; c) 1670°C. X500 (after Galasso et al[9]).

In an independent study, Galasso, Kuehl and Tice[8] also examined fragments of boron fiber with an electron microscope. The fragments exhibited
conchoidal fractures and exhibited no Bragg diffraction contrast effects
associated with crystalline materials at magnifications of X100,000 even
when the fragments were tilted in different directions using both bright
field and dark field techniques. See Fig. 2.4 Selected area electron
diffraction patterns of the boron fragments showed the same broad rings
characteristics of amorphous boron. See Fig. 2.5. These results indicate
that the boron is amorphous, but the difference in these results by different workers leaves doubt as to the exact nature of the boron in the
fibers.

When higher deposition temperatures are employed crystalline boron
is formed. Between 1400° and 1500°C the boron is deposited in the
β-tetragonal form, and above 1500°C the boron is deposited in the
β-rhombohedral form. In the range 1400° to 1500°C the boron starts to
deposit as amorphous material and then crystalline in later deposition
stages.[9] The amorphous material becomes crystalline during deposition
as is evidenced by the large equiaxed grains next to the core. Note the
columnar grains in Fig. 2.6. These are typical of pyrolytically deposited
crystalline material. Unlike amorphous boron fiber the surface of crystalline fibers are rough as shown in Fig. 2.7.

During deposition of boron, the tungsten substrate is completely converted to tungsten borides. In the initial stages of boron diffusion, WB,
W_2B_5 and a higher boride have been identified in X-ray patterns of the
fiber. By the time the fiber has grown to a 0.004 in. diameter, the core
contains only W_2B_5 and the higher boride, which recently has been determined to be WB_4.[10] Its X-ray pattern is given below in Table 2.1.

Table 2.1

X-RAY DATA FOR "WB$_4$"

hkl	d_{obs}	d_{calc}	I/I_o, obs	I/I_o, calc
100	4.49	4.50	W	25
101	3.66	3.67	S+	80
002	3.15	3.16	M	55
110, 102	2.58	2.59, 2.58	S	100
201	2.110	2.118	M	20
112	1.999	2.006	S+	90
103	1.903	1.907	M	15
211	1.638	1.641	M+	20
004	1.579	1.579	W+	10
203	1.535	1.537	W+	10
300, 212	1.497	1.498, 1.496	M	20
114, 302	1.352	1.349, 1.354	S+	50
213	1.323	1.322	W	10
220	1.298	1.298	W	10
303, 311	1.221	1.221, 1.223	W	5
222	1.201	1.200	M	20

Some studies also have been conducted using 0.0005 in. diameter molybdenum and 0.0012 in. diameter tantalum wire.[4] The boron was deposited on a resistively heated stationary tantalum wire at 1050°C. The boron in the fiber was amorphous and the core contained TaB_2 as well as unreacted tantalum. At present, the smallest diameter of the tantalum wire which can be purchased in quantity is too large to be of practical value. The results of boron deposition on 0.0005 in. diameter molybdenum wire were quite similar to those obtained using a tungsten substrate. The borides formed in the core of this fiber were identified as being Mo_2B_5 and MoB_4.

PROPERTIES

Boron fiber is particularly suitable for aerospace applications where low density is an important consideration. Pure boron has a density of only 2.34 g/cm^3, and 0.004 in. diameter boron fiber produced using a 0.0005 in. diameter tungsten substrate has a density of 2.6 g/cm^3. Boron fibers formed using a smaller substrate wire such as those produced by Wacker-Chemie have a density closer to that of pure boron.

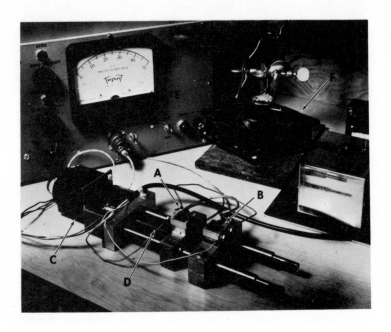

Fig. 2.8. Tensile Tester; A - moving crosshead hot plate; B - load cell hot plate; C - 1 rpm synchronous motor; D - drive screw; E - load indicator; and F - "muffin" fan (after Schile and Rosica[13]).

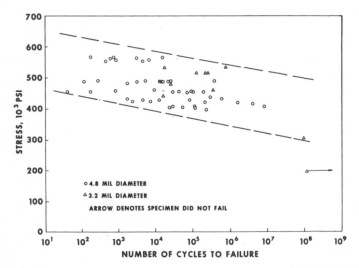

Fig. 2.9. Rotating beam fatigue of boron filament (after Salkind and Patarini[18]).

Boron fibers are extremely hard and have very high strengths and moduli. The hardness is greater than 9 on the Mohs scale and 4000 kg/mm^2 on the Vickers scale.[11] The average ultimate tensile strength of production boron is approximately 450,000 psi with some fibers having strengths as high as 600,000 psi. In a study of a sample production run, boron fiber with an average ultimate tensile strength of 536,000 psi, the standard deviation was found to be 31,500 psi.[12] The Poisson ratio for boron fiber is 0.21.

Tensile strength values of the boron fibers can be obtained using Instron testers, but in some laboratories, special equipment has been developed for this purpose. One of these is shown in Fig. 2.8.[13] In this apparatus the boron fiber is mounted between the moving crosshead (A) and a stationary crosshead (B) so as to provide a 1" gage length. The fiber is attached to the crossheads by sealing wax which is melted by Nichrome heaters underneath the filament mounting plates. The voltages from the load cells are read on the load indicator and converted to ultimate tensile strength values.

The minimum elastic modulus of commercial boron fiber has been established as 55×10^6 psi, and the average value is approximately 58×10^6 psi. This value was obtained from tests on production boron filament using a gage length of 10 inches. The measurements were made using a differential transformer extensometer clamped to the fiber using counterweights to prevent loading of the fiber, and a conventional strain gage tensile load cell. The stress-strain curves were obtained on an x-y recorder and the modulus was taken as the slope of the curve.

Improvements in the strength of boron fiber have been reported by Machonis[14] and Wawner[15] after electropolishing or etching with nitric acid. Wawner showed that by chemical etching tensile strength increases of from 100,000 psi to 200,000 psi could be attained in fibers with strengths of less than 400,000 psi and small strength increases could be attained in higher strength fibers. Etching also improved the flexural strength with a peak value of 2×10^6 psi being reported and individual values being measured as high as 2.7×10^6 psi.

These results relate well with those obtained from fracture studies which showed that fractures generally nucleate at the surface of weaker boron fibers and in the boron-tungsten boride core interface in the etched fibers.[14,16] In strong fibers, where the fracture is nucleated at the boron-tungsten boridecore interface, etching has little effect, while removal of surface flaws in weaker fibers results in significant fiber strengthening.

The shear modulus appears to be different for different boron fiber diameters. The shear modulus of 0.004 in. diameter boron fiber has been reported by Lasday and Talley[11] to be between 24 and 26×10^6 psi, while Herring and Krishna[17] obtained values of 20.2×10^6 psi for 0.0017 in. diameter fiber and 15.8 to 18.0×10^6 psi for 0.003 in. diameter fiber.

The fatigue resistance of boron fiber is quite good. This can be seen in the data reported by Salkind and Patarini[18] in Fig. 2.9. The data were obtained using a commercial rotating beam wire fatigue tester in which one end of the test sample is held in a chuck in a synchronous motor, bent in a "U" shape and the other end inserted in a carbide bushing. Samples were rotated at 3600 rpm and an automatic shutoff device was used to determine the number of cycles to failure. The samples which failed exhibited catastrophic failure, but with no permanent deformation.

The coefficient of thermal expansion for boron fiber has been measured to be 2.6-$2.8 \times 10^{-6}/°F$ over the range of room temperature to 600°F.[11,16] This is about half the value for bulk crystalline boron.

The effect of one hour heat treatment in argon on the room temperature strength of boron fiber is shown in Fig. 2.10.[9] The fibers were

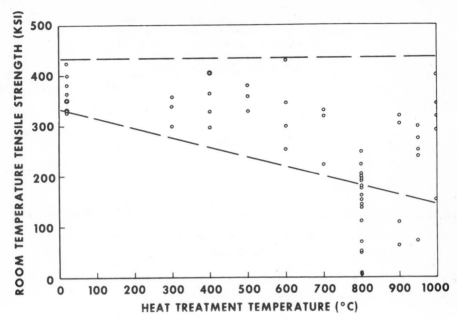

Fig. 2.10. Effect of heat treatment (argon) on room temperature tensile strength of boron filaments (after Galasso et al[9]).

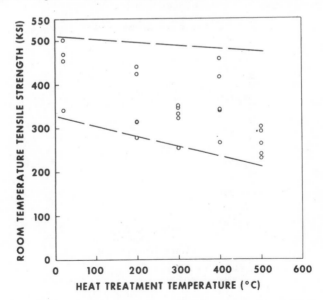

Fig. 2.11. Effect of heat treatment (air) on room temperature tensile strength of boron filaments (after Galasso et al[9]).

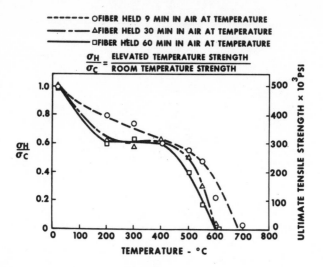

Fig. 2.12. Strength retention vs. temperature for boron fibers (after Veltri and Galasso[21]).

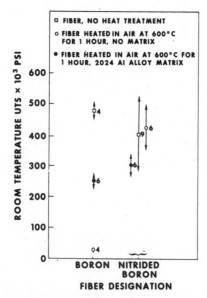

Fig. 2.13. Room temperature ultimate tensile strength for boron and nitrided boron fiber before and after heat treatment (after Jacob et al[23]).

heated in purified flowing argon gas and the room temperature strength
was then measured. In general, the effect of the heating was to increase
the scatter of the tensile strength data but the fibers were not severely
degraded at temperatures up to 700°C. Even at temperatures up to 1000°C
many of the fibers retained considerable strength. The general results of
this study agree with those reported by Herring.[19]

Ellison and Boone[20] have shown that boron fiber is quite creep resistant, being better than tungsten wire.

When boron fiber is heated in air for an hour, the room temperature
strength is not drastically reduced until it is heated above 500°C.[9] See
Fig. 2.11. Above 500°C, the oxide which formed on the boron fiber at
lower temperatures becomes fluid and flows allowing rapid oxidation of
boron. This oxidation results in severe degradation of the fibers.

Ultimate tensile strength measurements on boron fibers have also been
made in air at elevated temperatures.[21] Fibers were held at temperature
for 9, 30 and 60 minutes and then tested. The data are plotted in Fig.
2.12. The strength of boron fiber decreases as the temperature is increased
with the most degradation taking place above 500°C. In the range of 200°
to 400°C the strength of the boron fiber levels off at 60% of the room
temperature strength. The variation in the strength of boron fiber with
time of exposure, shown in Fig. 2.12, corresponds to the behavior of boron
in air at elevated temperatures. Below 500°C, the boric oxide impedes
continuous oxidation of the boron, and as was mentioned previously, above
500°C the oxide becomes viscous and flows leaving the surface exposed to
the air. Boron fiber continues to oxidize at temperatures above 500°C
until it is completely degraded.

The modulus of boron fibers also has been measured at elevated
temperatures.[20] At 1200°F, the modulus was found to be 35 x 10^6 psi

and at 1500°F a value of 32 x 10^6 psi was measured. These values were
not found to vary significantly for boron fibers of different diameters.

COATED BORON FIBERS

While boron fiber has excellent room temperature properties and can
withstand elevated temperatures in an inert atmosphere, its strength in
air at elevated temperatures is reduced especially at temperatures above
500°C. In addition, boron is very reactive and, hence, interacts with
metal matrices causing serious degradation of the fiber.

Two approaches have been tried to protect the boron fiber. One involved nitriding the surface of the boron[22,23] and the other involved
coating the boron fibers with silicon carbide.[24] Camahort[22] nitrided a
boron fiber and showed that the coating served as a barrier in molten
aluminum for 10 minutes at 800°C. In addition, he indicated that the
coating prevented attack of the fiber by powdered 2024 aluminum alloy at
elevated temperatures.

Since Camahort's studies were conducted using low strength fiber
(produced in the early stages of boron fiber development) and the compatibility studies were conducted in the absence of air, Jacob et al[23]
nitrided currently produced higher strength boron fiber and carried out
compatibility studies in air. They found that heating the boron fiber
in a mixture of ammonia and hydrogen produced a nitride coating which
offers protection for boron in air and in 2024 aluminum powder in air for
1 hr at 600°C. See Fig. 2.13. The strength of boron fiber is reduced
slightly by the nitriding process, but this can be tolerated if high
temperature protection is needed. However, at times greater than 1 hr
at 600°C in air the strength of the nitrided boron fiber begins to degrade.
Thus, these fibers appear to be most suitable for short time exposures
at elevated temperatures in air such as those used in the preparation of
composites.

Fig. 2.14. Photomicrograph of polished and etched cross section of silicon carbide coated boron fiber (after Basche et al[24]).

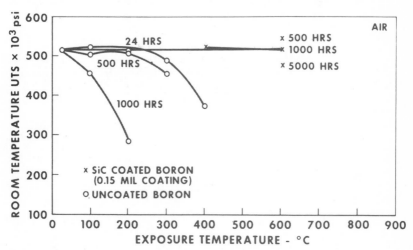

Fig. 2.15. Average room temperature ultimate tensile strength of filaments after being heated in air (after Basche et al[24]).

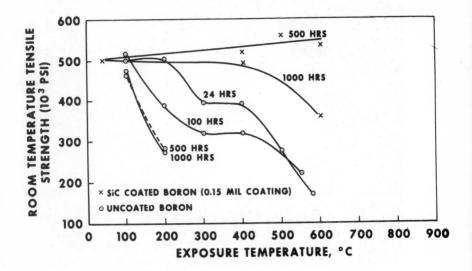

Fig. 2.16. Average room temperature ultimate tensile strength of filaments after being heated in 2024 aluminum alloy in air (after Basche et al[24]).

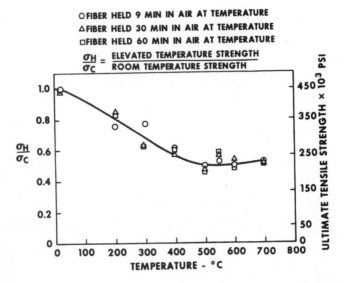

Fig. 2.17. Strength retention vs. temperature for silicon carbide coated boron fibers (after Veltri and Galasso[21]).

A silicon carbide coating on boron fiber offers much more protection.
Borsic fiber produced by Hamilton Standard contains a silicon carbide coating a fraction of a mil in thickness. A cross section is shown in Fig.
2.14. The coating is applied using chemical vapor deposition and methyldichlorosilane as the reactant gas. The X-ray diffraction pattern indicated that the boron remained "amorphous" and the silicon carbide was of
the β form preferentially oriented so that the { 111 } planes were parallel
to the fiber axis.

The tensile strength and modulus of the silicon carbide coated boron
fiber are nearly the same as that of boron fiber. The strength is retained even after the fiber is heated in air at 600°C for 1000 hrs. This
can be contrasted with compatibility data for uncoated boron fibers in
Fig. 2.15. Silicon carbide coated boron fibers also retained their room
temperature strength after being exposed to 2024 aluminum alloy in air at
500°C. Similar results were obtained for tests in titanium powder in the
absence of air. These data are plotted with compatibility data for boron
fiber in Fig. 2.16. It should be noted that after extremely long times,
such as 1000 hrs, silicon carbide coated boron fiber in a metal matrix
will begin to degrade.

Unlike boron fiber, the high temperature strength of the silicon
carbide coated boron fiber does not vary with different holding times
(9, 30 and 60 minutes) at the testing temperatures.[21] See Fig. 2.17.
However, the strength of the coated fiber does decrease in much the same
way as that of boron fiber below 500°C, but from 500°C to 700°C its
strength remains nearly constant.

In Chapter 5, the boron-epoxy composites are discussed. The combina-
tion of high strength, high modulus and low density of these composites
have helped to create the interest which is continuously growing for these
types of materials. For higher temperature applications, the silicon

carbide coated boron-metal matrix composites are being developed as tapes and multilayer composites. The oxidation resistance and inertness of these fibers allow fabrication processes to be used which would cause degradation of the uncoated boron fiber, and also permit the composites to be used at 600°F for long periods of time.

REFERENCES

1. E. Weintraub, J. Ind. Eng. Chem., 3, 299 (1911).

2. C. P. Talley, L. Line, and Q. Overman, Boron Synthesis, Structure, and Properties, J. Kohn, W. Nye, and G. Gaule eds., Plenum Press, New York (1960).

3. R. B. Reeves and J. J. Gebhardt, SAMPE, 10th National Symposium, San Diego, November (1966).

4. F. Galasso and J. Pinto, Trans. AIME, 242, 754 (1968).

5. R. Bourdeau, Private Communication.

6. J. S. Gillespie, Jr., J. Am. Chem. Soc., 88:11, 2423 (1966).

7. H. M. Otte and H. A. Lipsitt, Phys. Stat. Sol., 13, 439 (1966).

8. F. Galasso, D. Kuehl and W. Tice, J. of Appl. Phys., 38, 414 (1967).

9. F. Galasso, M. Salkind, D. Kuehl, and V. Patarini, Trans. AIME, 236, 1748 (1966).

10. F. Galasso and A. Paton, Trans. AIME, 236, 1751 (1966).

11. A. Lasday and C. Talley, SAMPE, 10th National Symposium, San Diego, November, (1966).

12. C. Shulze, Private Communication.

13. R. Schile and G. Rosica, Rev. Sci. Instr., 38, 1103 (1967).

14. A. Machonis, Grumman Research Department Report RE-270, October (1966).

15. F. Wawner, Boron, Vol. 2, G. Gaule, ed., Plenum Press, New York, 283 (1965).

16. F. Wawner, Modern Composite Materials, L. Broutman and R. Krock, eds., Addison Wesley, Reading, 244 (1967).

17. H. W. Herring and V. G. Krishna, NASA-TM-X-1246, July (1966).

18. M. Salkind and V. Patarini, Trans. AIME, 239, 1268 (1967).

19. H. W. Herring, NASA-TN-D-3202, January (1966).

20. E. G. Ellison and D. H. Boone, J. Less-Common Metals, 13, 103 (1967).

21. R. Veltri and F. Galasso, Nature, 220, 781 (1968).

22. J. L. Camahort, J. Composite Materials, 2, 104 (1968).

23. B. Jacob, R. Bourdeau and F. Galasso, Fibre Science and Technology,
     2, 243 (1969).

24. M. Basche, R. Fanti and F. Galasso, Fibre Science and Technology,
     1, 19 (1968).

3

CARBON FIBERS

INTRODUCTION

    High modulus carbon fibers have been produced by carbonizing organic precursor fibers and then graphitizing them at a very high temperature. The most widely employed precursor fibers are polyacrylonitrile (PAN) and rayon fibers, but a number of other precursors such as polyvinylalcohol, polyimide, phenolics, and pitches have also been used. Rayon fiber can be converted to high modulus carbon fiber in the absence of oxygen, but polyacrylonitrile fiber requires slow oxidation at temperatures between 200° and $300^\circ C$ before pyrolysis to prevent melting.

    In both processes, preferential orientation is produced in the fiber by stretching at various stages of heating. This stretching results in a better alignment of the graphite layer planes in the final carbon fiber, which increases its modulus. Polyacrylonitrile is stretched in the early stages of carbon fiber formation, while in the rayon to high modulus carbon conversion stretching is applied during graphitization.

    The high modulus carbon fiber is of current interest as reinforcement in organic matrix composites which are being developed for aircraft structures and components, marine craft, and fan and compressor blades in jet engines. This latter application has captured the imagination of engine manufacturers in England and the United States who feel that significant weight savings can be achieved by replacing some of the conventional metals in the engines with carbon-epoxy resin composites.

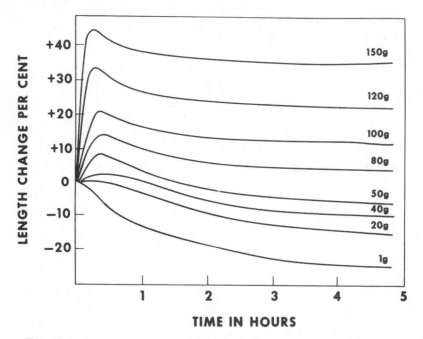

Fig. 3.1. Length changes of PAN fibers during oxidation at 220°C (after Watt and Johnson[3]).

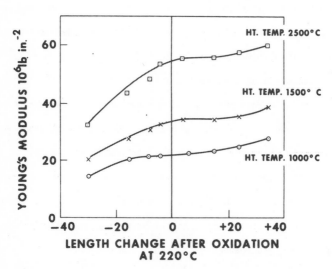

Fig. 3.2. Length changes after oxidation and Young's moduli of carbon fibers (after Watt and Johnson[3]).

PREPARATION

High modulus carbon fiber was first prepared from polyacrylonitrile by Shindo in 1961.[1] He produced a carbon fiber with a modulus of 24 x 10[6] psi. Later, workers at Rolls-Royce Limited found that the modulus of carbon fiber could be increased considerably by stretching the precursor polyacrylonitrile (PAN) fiber before the processing.[2] The PAN fiber in a tow form was stretched up to 400% in boiling water or steam at just over 100°C and then cooled to 15-20°C. This stretched fiber was heated to 1000°C in an inert gas to carbonize the fiber and then at a temperature above 2500°C to graphitize it. When the precursor fiber was preoxidized below 400°C, after stretching and before carbonization, values of as high as 85 x 10[6] psi were obtained for the modulus.

Studies at R.A.E. showed that increases in the modulus of carbon fiber also could be attained by stretching in the oxidation step.[3] In this work tows of commercial PAN fibers were also used as in the Rolls Royce investigations. The tows consisting of 700 filaments each were heated at 220°C in circulating air with weights of from 1 to 130 grams hanging from them. The changes in the lengths of the fibers after different oxidation times are shown in Fig. 3.1. The oxidized fiber was then heated in argon to 1000°C at a rate of 125°C/hr, at 1500°C and finally at 2500°C. In Figure 3.2, the length change after oxidation of the fiber is plotted as a function of the modulus for different heating temperatures. It can be seen that the modulus of the carbon fiber increases with in-creased stretching of the precursor fiber during oxidation. Johnson et al[4] felt that this stretching would be useful whether the precursor used was pure PAN or a copolymer of acrylonitrile with methyl methacrylate or vinyl acetate.

Logsdail[5] at A.E.R.E., Harwell showed that stretching of the carbon fiber during graphitization also increased the modulus. He stretched the

fibers up to 7% under loads of 0.5, 1.0 and 2.0g per fiber at temperatures
of 2000°C, 2300°C and 2500°C. For the 0.5 and 1.0g per fiber load the increase in modulus was small, but the 2.0g per fiber load increased the
modulus 20% for a heat treatment temperature of 2500°C and 30% for a heat
treatment of 2000°C.

In the oxidation step, PAN fiber takes up about 8 weight % oxygen in
5 hours at 220°C while HCN and NH_3 are given off resulting in a carbon
yield of 45%. In dry air, 4% water is evolved when PAN fibers are oxidized
at 220°C and 4% more when they are carbonized in vacuum, Watt and Johnson[3]
postulate that the following reaction takes place.

In the formation of carbon fiber from a rayon precursor, the fiber
is first heated slowly up to 400°C. The fiber is then reacted rapidly to
about 1000°C and by stretching the carbon fiber at a temperature of 2500°C
or above during graphitization, high modulus fibers are attained.

During processing of an experimental 10×10^6 psi modulus carbon
fiber to a 100×10^6 psi modulus fiber, the strength was found to increase
from 120×10^3 psi to 500×10^3 psi, the fracture strain decreased from
1% to 1/2%, the conductivity increased from 400 ohm-cm^{-1} to 1750 ohm-cm^{-1},
and the density increased from 1.35 g/cm^3 to 1.95 g/cm^3.[6]

In the HITCO method of producing high modulus carbon fiber, carbon
fiber is prepared in a similar manner to that described previously for
rayon based fiber except that the carbon fiber is heated electrically
while being stretched instead of by radiant heating. In a technique described by Gibson and Langlois,[7] the rayon yarn enters a heating tube (A)
and makes a double pass around graphite electrodes. See Fig. 3.3. Once

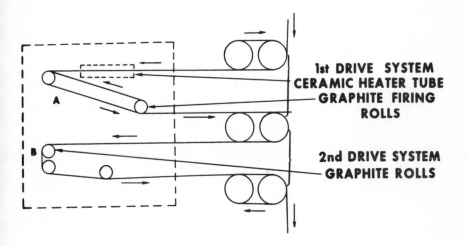

Fig. 3.3. Schematic diagram of electro-process equipment (after Gibson and Langlois[7]).

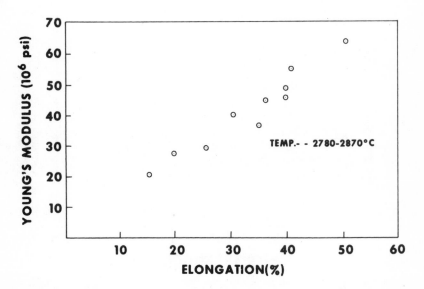

Fig. 3.4. Effect of elongation upon Young's modulus (after Gibson and Langlois[7]).

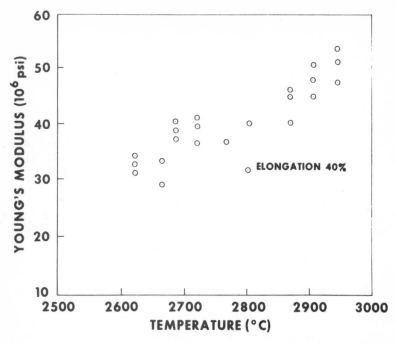

Fig. 3.5. Effect of temperature upon Young's modulus (after Gibson and Langlois[7]).

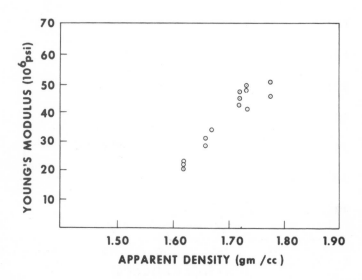

Fig. 3.6. Relationship of Young's modulus and apparent density (after Gibson and Langlois[7]).

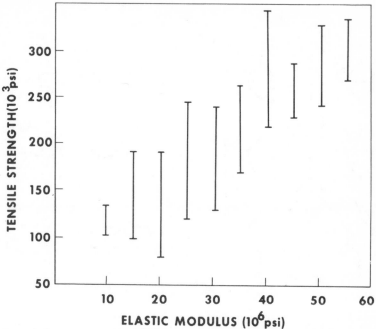

Fig. 3.7. Relationship of tensile strength and Young's modulus (after Gibson and Langlois[7]).

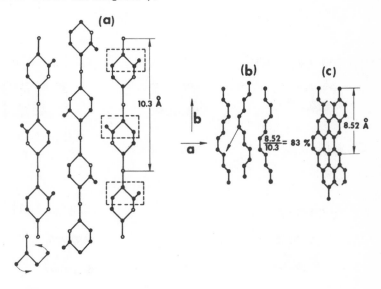

Fig. 3.8. Geometry of the "longitudinal polymerization process" of cellulose ring unit residues into graphite layers (after Bacon and Tang[8]).

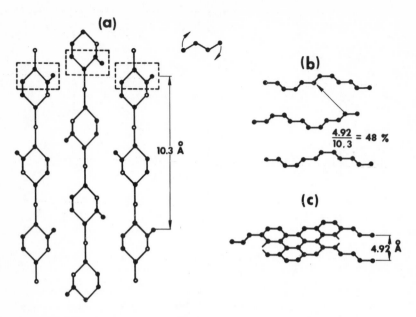

Fig. 3.9. Geometry of the "transverse polymerization process" of cellulose ring unit residues into graphite layers (after Bacon and Tang[8]).

UNION CARBIDE

THORNEL-50

HITCO

HMG-40

CARBORUNDUM

LOW MODULUS
GRAPHITE YARN

COURTAULDS

TYPE B

MORGANITE

TYPE I

Fig. 3.10. Photomicrographs of cross sections of carbon fibers.

the fiber becomes conducting, it can be heated resistively and the yarn
on the first pass is heated to a conductive state by the heated yarn on
the second pass. Then, the yarn is heated to very high temperatures as it
passes over electrodes (B) while it is elongated by the second drive
system.

The effect of elongation during graphitization on modulus is shown
in Fig. 3.4. It can be seen that both stretching and high temperatures of
graphitization increase the modulus (Fig. 3.4 and 3.5). At higher temperatures the pore content decreases and the density of the fiber increases.
The relationship between modulus and density and modulus and tensile
strength can be seen in Figs. 3.6 and 3.7. Unlike the PAN based fiber,
the strength of carbon fiber formed from rayon fiber increases with increasing modulus at graphitization temperatures up to 3000°C.

Bacon and Tang[8] have proposed geometrical schemes to explain the
transition from rayon to carbon fiber. They are based on a yield of four
carbon atoms from each cellulose ring which results in a 29.6% weight
yield of carbon. In a longitudinal polymerization scheme they predict an
83% length yield and in transverse polymerization a 48% yield. See Figs.
3.8 and 3.9. It is interesting, that by stretching the precursor fiber,
a length yield of 76% in the graphitized fiber is approached suggesting
the predominance of longitudinal polymerization in an oriented fiber,
and studies on a model rayon system yielded 27 to 29.5 wt% carbon in the
final filament. Both of these results agree well with those predicted by
Bacon and Tang.

MICROSTRUCTURE AND STRUCTURE

The cross sections of the fibers produced from rayon are irregular in
shape, while those formed from PAN are nearly round. See Fig. 3.10. The
effect of the two types of surfaces on the properties of the fibers has
not been determined.

Fig. 3.11. Electron micrograph of cross section of a carbon fiber.

Fig. 3.12. Electron micrograph of longitudinal section of a carbon fiber.

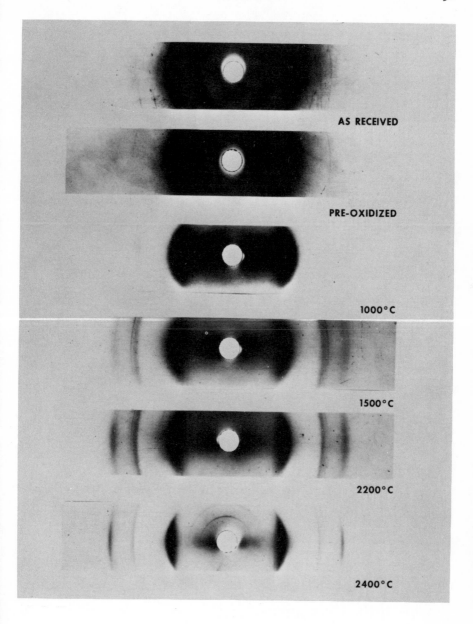

Fig. 3.13. X-ray diffraction photographs of polyacrylonitrile yarn,
as received, and in various processing stages.

Electron photomicrographs of cross sections and longitudinal sections of the carbon fibers, Figs. 3.11 and 3.12, reveal that they consist of a network of fibrils and elongated pores strung along the length of the fiber. These fibrils appear to be derived from the original raw textile structure. For a 60×10^6 psi modulus carbon fiber, the fibrils measure 100Å across and have an undetermined length. Johnson and Watt[9] feel that the modulus of the carbon fiber is dependent on the orientation of the graphite crystallite in the fibrils while the strength is determined by the inter-fibrillar bonding.

X-ray diffraction photographs of the fibers during various stages of processing PAN fiber to carbon fiber are shown in Fig. 3.13. Note that the structure in the PAN fiber is destroyed during oxidation and at 1000°C the (002) reflection of graphite is seen. As the fiber is heated to higher temperatures the reflection from the fiber becomes sharper indicating a growth in the crystallites and some of the (hkl) reflections appear showing that the carbon layers are becoming aligned. Shindo[1] reported that crystallites grow in the a and c directions as the heat treating temperature is increased. The values he obtained for temperatures of 1000, 1500, 2500 and 3000°C were 39, 56, 110 and 200Å for L_a and 14, 22, 64 and 86Å for L_c.

Even after high temperature treatments during graphitization the crystallites in the carbon fiber are still turbostratic.[10] The d spacing as determined from the (002) X-ray pattern reflection is 3.39Å. This spacing which represents the distance between carbon layers decreases with increasing treatment temperatures, but it is always larger than the 3.35Å value found for natural graphite.

Bacon and Schalomon[6] measured the degree of preferred orientation in graphite fibers by measuring the intensity of X-ray reflection along the (002) arc. They took the half width of the bell-shaped intensity distribution at half maximum intensity as an indication of the relative degree

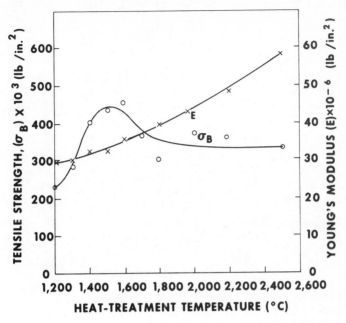

Fig. 3.14. Effect of heat treatment temperature on the mechanical properties of carbon fibers at room temperature (after Moreton et al[11]).

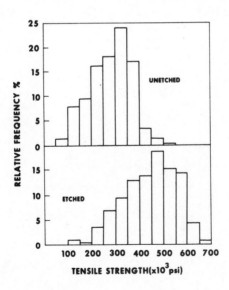

Fig. 3.15. Strength comparison between etched and unetched carbonized fiber (after Johnson[14]).

Table 3.1

PROPERTIES OF CARBON FILAMENTS

Supplier	Grade	Precursor	Tensile Strength (10³ psi)	Modulus (10⁶ psi)	Density (gm/cc)	Form
Union Carbide	T-25	Rayon	180	25	1.4-1.45	yarn
	T-40	Rayon	250	40	1.56	yarn
	T-50	Rayon	285	50	1.60	yarn
HITCO	HMG-25	Rayon	160-190	22-30	1.5	yarn
	HMG-40	Rayon	200-235	35-50	1.7	yarn
	HMG-50	Rayon	300-315	50-61	1.8	yarn
Courtaulds	Type A	PAN	275-325	28-33	1.8-1.9	meter tow 1000'
	Type B	PAN	250-300	50-60	1.9-2.0	meter tow 1000'
	Type C	PAN	325-375	35-40	1.9	meter tow 1000'
Morganite	Type 1	PAN	225-275	56-64	1.95	meter tow
	Type 2	PAN	370-430	36-40	1.75	meter tow
Kureha		Pitch	75-250	4-38	1.6-1.7	yarn 30-70 meters
Nippon Kayaku	G.L.	Lignine	85		1.8	meters

of disorientation of the graphite layer from alignment with the fiber axis. This value is found to be about 25° for low modulus graphite fiber, 10° for 40×10^6 psi fiber, and 5° for 80×10^6 psi fiber. In the intermediate range of modulus values, the "half width" of the (002) reflection can be used as an indication of the modulus.

PROPERTIES

The carbon fibers sold commercially are approximately 0.3 mil in diameter. The PAN filaments are processed as tows containing 10,000 fibers while rayon fiber is used in a two ply construction, with 770 filaments per ply. The carbon fiber produced from PAN is sold in meter and 1000 foot lengths.

A list of the companies which produce carbon fibers and the properties of the fibers are listed in Table 3.1. Note that the densities of carbon fibers prepared from rayon are lower than those prepared from PAN fibers; typical values are ∽1.6 g/cm^3 and 1.9 g/cm^3 respectively. The density increases with increasing modulus as shown by the values for "Thornel"-25, 40 and 50, which are 1.43, 1.56 and 1.63 g/cm^3.

The strength of carbon fiber decreases during oxidation or heating in an inert atmosphere with increasing temperatures to 400°C and above 400°C, the strength increases with rising temperatures. During graphitization both the modulus and strength of carbon fibers produced from rayon increase with increasing temperature. However, when PAN is used as the precursor fiber the strength of the resulting carbon fiber increases up to temperatures of 1500°C, decreases to 1900°C and then levels off, while the modulus increases continuously with increasing temperature over the entire graphitization temperatures. See Fig. 3.14. If a stress is applied on the fibers at the graphitization temperatures, the strength will increase with the modulus.[12]

Because the plate-like crystallites are so small (L_c = 100$\overset{o}{A}$ and L_a = 200$\overset{o}{A}$) and misoriented in the fibrils so that they are constrained, it was calculated that carbon fibers could have a modulus of $\sim$160 x 10^6 psi which exceeds the single crystal "a" axis modulus (130 x 10^6 psi).[12] While this value has not been achieved experimentally, some fibers have been reported with modulus values of 105 x 10^6 psi.

Brydges et al[13] postulate that the amount of constraint in crystallites in the carbon fibers is determined by the bonding between them. Since Poisson's ratio between a-axis strain and c-axis strain is -2, pulling the fiber extends the crystallite in the "a" direction and tries to contract it in the "c" direction. This contraction is resisted by a neighboring crystal which is being forced to contract in the "a" direction, because it is bonded at an angle to the first crystal. Therefore good bonding between these crystallites should result in maximum constraint and higher moduli.

While very high values of tensile strength have been reported for experimental carbon fibers the more common values are closer to 300,000 psi. In a study of carbon fibers produced from PAN fibers, Johnson[14] found that the carbon fibers fractured from internal and surface flaws. He showed that the voids were diconic in shape and postulated that these voids probably could be traced to foreign bodies or cavities in the original polymer. When the fiber was etched to remove the surface flaws, the mean strength of the fibers was improved. See Fig. 3.15. This flaw controlling mechanism appears to be active up to 1200-1300°C (treatment temperature). Above these temperatures, the failure mechanism may be controlled by other factors. These studies show the importance of starting with as pure and homogeneous a precursor fiber as possible.

REFERENCES

1. A. Shindo, Report No. 317 Gove. Industrial Res. Inst. Osaka (1961).

2. A. E. Steindage and R. Prescott, Rolls-Royce Limited Patent - Fibres Carbonneres A. Haute Resistance et a Module Eleve.

3. W. Watt and W. Johnson, Paper presented at Am. Chem. Soc. Meeting, Atlantic City, September (1968).

4. W. Johnson, L. Phillips and W. Watt, English Patent 1, 110, 791 April (1965).

5. D. H. Logsdail, Paper presented at Am. Chem. Soc. Meeting, Atlantic City, September (1968).

6. R. Bacon and W. A. Schalamon, Paper presented at Am. Chem. Soc. Meeting, Atlantic City, September (1968).

7. D. W. Gibson and G. B. Langlois, Paper presented at Am. Chem. Soc. Meeting, Atlantic City, September (1968).

8. R. Bacon and M. M. Tang, Carbon, 2, 221 (1964).

9. W. Johnson and W. Watt, Nature, 215, 384 (1967).

10. D. V. Badami, J. C. Joiner and G. A. Jones, Nature, 215, 386 (1967).

11. R. Moreton, W. Watt and W. Johnson, Nature, 213, 690 (1967).

12. J. W. Johnson, J. R. Marjoram and P. G. Rose, Nature, 221, 357 (1969).

13. W. T. Brydges, D. V. Badami, J. C. Joiner and G. A. Jones, Paper presented at Am. Chem. Soc. Meeting, Atlantic City, September (1968).

14. J. W. Johnson, Paper presented at Am. Chem. Soc. Meeting, Atlantic City, September (1968).

OTHER HIGH MODULUS FIBERS

INTRODUCTION

Boron and carbon fibers which are produced commercially are the most widely used low density-high modulus fibers. Silicon carbide, boron carbide, titanium diboride, boron nitride, alumina, zirconia and beryllium fibers are in various stages of development.

SILICON CARBIDE FIBER

It has been recognized that silicon carbide fibers would be extremely valuable for high temperature applications if they could be produced with properties equivalent to those of boron fibers. General Technology conducted extensive investigations to develop a process for preparing silicon carbide fiber with high strength and modulus.[1] They investigated $SiCl_4$ + C_7H_8, $SiCl_4$ + C_3H_2, $SiCl_4$ + CH_3I, $SiBr_4$ + C_2H_2, SiI_4 + C_2H_6, $HSiCl_3$ + CO, CH_3SiCl_3, $C_2H_5SiCl_3$, $(CH_3)_4Si$ and Cl_2CH_3SiH as possible reactant gases for SiC deposition on a resistively heated tungsten wire held at 1500°C. Initial experiments were conducted in a batch process in which a silicon halide was used as a source of silicon and a carbon containing gas was added. In these studies, hot spots would occur on the tungsten wire during deposition, and the wire would break. Using wires such as titanium, nichrome, and molybdenum as the substrate did not improve conditions. The fibers which could be recovered from the reactor were too weak to evaluate.

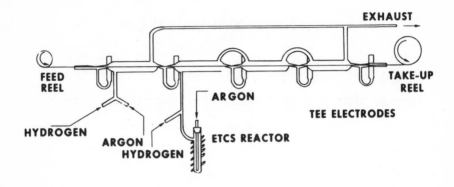

Fig. 4.1. Continuous deposition apparatus for production of silicon carbide filament (after Withers et al[1]).

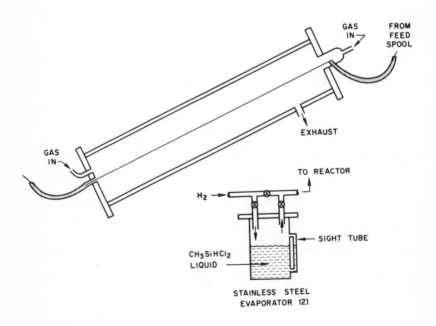

Fig. 4.2. Horizontal reactor for silicon carbide fiber production (after Galasso et al[2]).

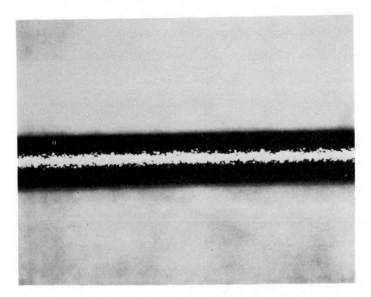

Fig. 4.3. Photomicrograph of surface of silicon carbide filament (after Galasso et al[2]).

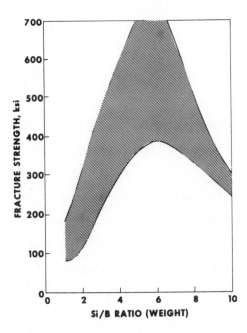

Fig. 4.4. Effect of boron content on tensile strength of silicon carbide fibers (after Elkins et al[3]).

From a study using other gases each of which contained both silicon and carbon, it was determined that SiC could be produced from Cl_2CH_3SiH at the lowest temperatures but the best properties were attained for fibers prepared using $C_2H_5SiCl_3$ and CH_3SiCl_3. In experiments in which methyl-trichlorosilane was used as the reactant gas the density of the silicon carbide was found to be greatest at a reaction temperature of 1100°C.

While both reactants were used equally in the experimental studies, because of its availability in larger quantities, $C_2H_5SiCl_3$ (ETCS) was used in preference to CH_3SiCl_3 in production. Fig. 4.1 shows the unit which was employed in the preparation of the silicon carbide fibers. A 10% $C_2H_5SiCl_3$ mixture with hydrogen and a temperature of 1200°C were found to be the best conditions for fiber preparation. The fibers produced had an average modulus of 68×10^6 psi and the average density of a 0.004 in. diameter SiC filament prepared on a 0.0005 in. diameter tungsten wire substrate was 3.35 g/cm^3. This fiber could be formed in a 30 inch reactor at a rate of 2 ft/min.

Researchers at United Aircraft Research Laboratories also examined a number of gaseous reactants for forming silicon carbide fibers and decided to use methyldichlorosilane in their process because it gave the fastest deposition rate and it was felt that the reaction rate had to be faster than that attained with $C_2H_5SiCl_3$ to be practical.[2] Using this process in the single chamber horizontal reactor shown in Fig. 4.2, or a vertical reactor silicon carbide fiber was prepared with a strength of 400,000 psi and a modulus of 55×10^6 psi. However, in production the average strength was 300,000 psi. Using a two chamber reactor, much faster growth rates could be attained for the same total length single stage reactor.

The surface of the silicon carbide filaments is shown in Fig. 4.3. Nodules are present on the surface, but they are smaller than those found

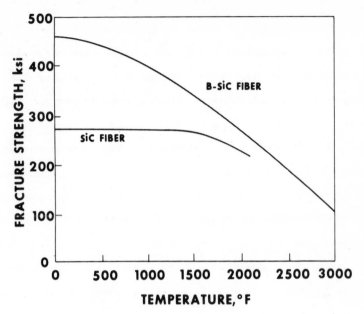

Fig. 4.5. Silicon carbide filament strength vs. temperature (after
Elkins et al[3]).

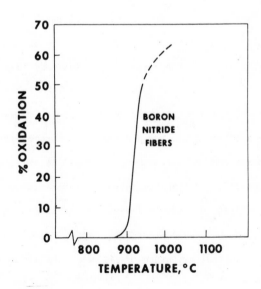

Fig. 4.6 Oxidation of boron nitride fibers at 500°/hr temperature
rise (after Economy and Anderson[5]).

on boron fibers. X-ray diffraction photographs of the fibers showed that
the silicon carbide was the β form (cubic) and it was preferentially
deposited so that the $\{111\}$ planes were parallel to the fiber axis.

Workers at Marquardt reported that they could produce much higher
strength fibers by adding boron to the depositing SiC to keep the grains
small.[3] In this process, boron trichloride and hydrogen gases were added
with the silane into a two chamber reactor. The 0.0005 in. diameter tungsten substrate was held at about 1100°C, and the pressure was maintained
at 125 mm to 200 mm of Hg. The fiber was drawn through the reactor at
20 in./min.

The effect of composition on the strength of the fibers is shown in
Fig. 4.4. It can be seen that the optimum composition of silicon to boron
is about 6.

The surface of the best fibers was smooth in comparison to the typical
corn cob appearance obtained when no boron was added and no grains could
be seen in photomicrographs of cross sections. X-ray diffraction photographs of the fibers showed the diffuse pattern of β-SiC and the pattern
of tungsten. Other lines in the x-ray pattern belonged to various forms
of α-SiC.

The strength of these fibers has been as high as 500,000 psi and the
modulus up to 65×10^6 psi, but the average strength and modulus is lower.
At elevated temperatures the strength of the fiber is reduced, but it still
retains nearly one fifth of its room temperature strength at 1650°C. The
strength of pure silicon carbide is lower, but at higher temperatures the
strength is about the same as that of Marquardt's fiber. See Fig. 4.5.
The coefficient of thermal expansion of silicon carbide fibers is
3.76×10^{-6}/°C.

Tyco, under a Naval contract, has been trying to reduce the density
and price of silicon carbide fiber by the deposition of SiC on fused

silica fiber instead of tungsten wire. The heating source being used is a double elliptical mirror furnace employing line source tungsten infrared lamps and the substrate is carbon coated glass. Strengths of 200,000 psi and moduli of 60×10^6 psi have been obtained by this process. However, obtaining fibers with uniform strength, using carbon coated glass fiber, is much more difficult than by the conventional method which employs tungsten wire as the substrate.

BORON NITRIDE FIBER

Boron nitride fibers have been considered for use in composites because they are stable to 850°C in an oxidizing atmosphere (Fig. 4.6), can have strengths of 200,000 psi and a density of only 1.8 g/cm^3.[4,5] These fibers are available from the Carborundum Company with diameters of 5 to 8 microns and in lengths up to 15 inches. They are circular in cross section, uniform in diameter and appear to be transparent. Because of the low density compared to the theoretical value of 2.25 g/cm^3, it is felt that the fibers may contain very fine micropores. Only their low modulus of $6-10 \times 10^6$ psi keeps them from being used more extensively as reinforcement in composites.

Recently, Economy et al[6] reported that they had prepared boron nitride fibers by a novel technique involving the nitriding of a boric oxide fiber. They reacted ammonia with boric oxide fiber above 200°C to form the compound $(B_2O_3)_xNH_3$. This permitted the fiber to be heated to higher temperatures while the nitriding was continued up to 1000°C. X-ray patterns of the fibers in various stages showed that the boron nitride layers were beginning to form below 1000°C and above 1000°C the graphitic type structure became more perfect.

In the graphitization of boron nitride fibers the crystallite sizes can be varied from 20-30Å to more than 1000Å.[7] The best fibers are produced with crystallite sizes of 60-160Å and diameters of 9 microns.

BORON CARBIDE FIBERS

Boron carbide, B_4C, fiber can be prepared by passing an equimolar mixture of boron trichloride and hydrogen with 2% toluene vapor over a molybdenum or carbon substrate at 800°C to 1200°C.[8] Hough and Golf[9] reported the formation of boron carbide fibers using carboranes with the general formula $B_nC_2H_{n+2}$. In a series of experiments they pyrolyzed carborane-10 $(B_{10}C_2H_{12})$ and carborane derivatives on a 0.010 inch diameter tungsten wire. The deposit was nodular when argon was employed as a carrier gas and smoother when hydrogen was used. Materials produced at temperatures below 1000°C, gave either a weak or no halo pattern in their x-ray photographs and exhibited brittle fractures while those prepared at depositing temperatures between 1000°C and 1300°C, gave an amorphous halo x-ray pattern and showed a glass-like fracture.

Fibers for property measurements were produced on 0.0005 in. diameter tungsten wire in the apparatus drawn in Fig. 4.7. The density of the deposits was found to be 2.48 g/cm^3, from which it was deduced that the deposit contained 60 vol % $B_{13}C_2$ and 40 vol % $B_{12}C_3$. The strength of fibers produced at 1040°C with diameters of 0.00734 inches was 113,400 psi and the modulus was measured to be 40×10^6 psi. At present, the strengths of the boron carbide fibers are quite low but the low temperature of deposition does make the process worthwhile investigating.

General Electric has investigated the preparation of B_4C fibers using BCl_3 and CH_4 gases and a tungsten substrate. They report that the boron carbide fiber is glassy, and has strengths up to 390,000 psi, moduli up to 62×10^6 psi and a density of 2.7 g/cm^3 for 0.0025 in. diameter fibers.

The preparation of boron carbide yarn (by reacting BCl_3 and hydrogen gases on a carbon yarn) has been reported by workers at Carborundum.[10] In the initial process a layer of boron carbide is formed and subsequent carbide formation depends on diffusion through this layer. Fibers were

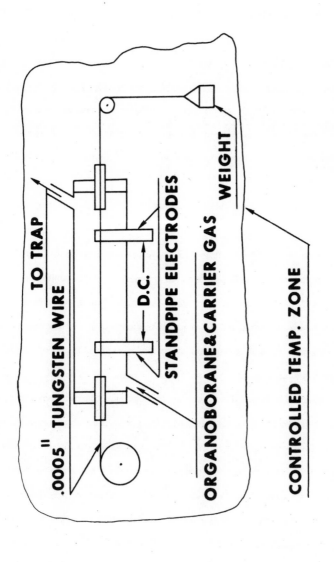

Fig. 4.7

prepared with different amounts of boron carbide. The density of these fibers varied from 1.55 g/cm^3 to 2.51 g/cm^3. In static runs, tensile strength values as high as 260,000 psi and elastic moduli of 60-70 x 10^6 psi have been attained.

TITANIUM DIBORIDE FIBERS

Titanium diboride fibers have been prepared by chemical vapor deposition using TiCl$_4$ and BCl$_3$ gases and a 0.0005 in. diameter tungsten substrate. The tensile strength and modulus of 0.004 in. diameter fiber has been reported to be 150 x 10^3 psi and 70 x 10^6 psi respectively.

OXIDE FIBERS

Tyco has developed a method of producing continuous aluminum oxide single crystals.[11] Fibers 0.009 inch in diameter have had an average tensile strength of 300,000 psi with high values of 500,000 psi and a modulus of 40 x 10^6 psi. They produce the sapphire fibers by drawing them from molten alumina contained in a molybdenum crucible. By using appropriate seeds, the fibers are grown in various crystallographic directions and in a variety of shapes such as tubes, ovals and ribbons.

H. I. Thompson Fiber Glass Co. has produced fibers of zirconia-calcia, zirconia-silica, zircon with 1% hafnia and alumina, and zirconia and hafnia by a "suspension method".[12]   Finely divided oxide is added to a carrier material, the resulting viscous fluid is spun forming a green fiber, and this fiber then is heated to remove the carrier material. Zirconia and zircon fibers prepared in this manner are not affected by exposures to temperatures of between 1320 and 2000°C.[13] The strength of the fibers is about 200,000 psi and the modulus is 25 x 10^6 psi for diameters of 0.0003 to 0.0008 in.

In another process for forming alumina fibers, fused silica tubes are packed with alumina, heated and drawn. The drawn fibers contain crystal-line alumina with a glass silica sheath. Elastic moduli up to 20×10^6 psi have been reported for this type of fiber.[14]

Continuous lengths of alumina, zircon, and alumina lithia spinels have been produced by Horizons.[15,16,17] For alumina fibers, a 50 wt% solution of aluminum formoacetate $Al(OH)(CHO_2)(C_2H_3O_2)$ is warmed to 80°C and dried under vacuum. Streams of solution emerge from the spinnerette and are dried with warm air to form a fiber. As the fibers emerge, they are drawn from a diameter of 127 microns to 10 to 25 microns and wound on a drum. This fiber is then heated slowly to 1500°C. The alumina fiber is amorphous when it is first rolled on the drum, becomes crystalline in the gamma form at 1000°C and above 1000°C transforms to alpha aluminum oxide. Care is taken during this transformation to prevent the growth of large grains which could weaken the fiber.

In order to form alumina-lithia spinel, a lithium organic compound is added to the spinning solution. The size of the grains in this fiber is maintained at about 67Å.

The preparation of these oxide fibers is important because they could be used in composites which would be suitable at very high temperatures. Reinforced ceramics and eutectic composites are the other possibilities to meet the high temperature requirements. Although continuous oxide fila-ments have not been available in quantity, there is still a great deal of information on oxide-metal systems which can be derived from the alumina whisker studies of Sutton and co-workers at the Missile and Space division of General Electric, and the work at Horizons, Inc. on nickel and iron base matrices. Both of these investigations have dealt with the bonding of alumina with metal matrices, which may be a major problem in eventually using these composites for high temperature applications.

REFERENCES

1. J. C. Withers, L. C. McCandless and R. T. Schwartz, SAMPE, 10th
    National Symposium, San Diego, November (1966).

2. F. Galasso, M. Basche and D. Kuehl, Appl. Phys. Letters, 9, 37 (1966).

3. P. E. Elkins, G. M. Mallan, H. Shimizer, SAMPE, 10th National
    Symposium, San Diego, November (1966).

4. J. Economy and R. V. Anderson, Symposium on High Temperature Fibers,
    ACS Winter Meeting, Phoenix, Arizona, January (1966).

5. J. Economy, R. V. Anderson and D. T. Meloon, SAMPE, 10th National
    Symposium, San Diego, November (1966).

6. J. Economy, R. V. Anderson and V. I. Matkovich, Paper Presented at
    Am. Chem. Soc. Meeting, Atlantic City, September (1968).

7. J. Economy and R. V. Anderson, J. Pol. Sci., Part C, 283 (1967).

8. C. F. Powell, I. E. Cambell and B. W. Gonser, Vapor-Plating, John
    Wiley and Sons, Inc., New York, 72 (1962).

9. R. Hough and L. C. Golf, SAMPE, 10th National Symposium, San Diego,
    November (1966).

10. D. J. Beerntsen, W. D. Smith, J. Economy, Paper Presented at Am. Chem.
    Soc. Meeting, Atlantic City, September (1968).

11. New York Times, October 22 (1967).

12. B. T. Fellows and J. P. Sterry, Am. Cer. Soc. Symp., Philadelphia,
    May (1965).

13. J. P. Sterry, Material in Design Engineering, 12, October (1962).

14. H. D. Batha and S. D. Mark, Industrial Research, 89, February (1967).

15. R. Lockhart, ASTM Committee Meeting, D-30, Philadelphia, October
    (1965).

16. R. H. Kelsey, U. S. Patent 3,270,109, August (1966).

17. R. S. Lockhart and E. Wainer, U. S. Patent 3,271,173, September (1966).

COMPOSITES

INTRODUCTION

"Man made" composites are prepared by placing fibers in a suitable matrix, while "natural" or eutectic composites are formed in a single solidification process. Some "man made" composites have been made with ceramic matrices, but recent efforts have been concentrated on organic and lightweight metal matrices for aerospace applications. The role of the matrix in these composites is to provide integrity and provide a means of distributing stress among the fibers.

ORGANIC MATRICES

Plastic matrices which are used in composites can be divided into the two categories, thermosetting and thermoplastic materials. A thermosetting material contains a three-dimensional network of atoms, and once it is formed, it is not softened by heating. A thermoplastic material, on the other hand, is made up of linear molecules with weak bonds between the chains, and can be softened by heating. Some of the thermosets are par- tially cured after being applied to the fibers. This "prepreg" material can be stored for long periods and then finally cured at a later date.

Polyesters and epoxy resins were borrowed from glass fiber reinforced composite technology as the matrices for high modulus fibers. A typical polyester has the formula

$$HO(CH_2 - CH_2 - O - \overset{\displaystyle O}{\overset{\displaystyle \|}{C}} - CH = CH - \overset{\displaystyle O}{\overset{\displaystyle \|}{C}} - O)_n - H$$

It can be prepared to be flexible and it can be mixed with rigid
resins to modify its properties. However, polyesters are more difficult to
handle than epoxy resins in the curing cycle and therefore, have not been
used as extensively as the epoxy resins.

A typical epoxy can have a density of 1.2 g/cm^3, a tensile strength of
5 to 14 x 10^3 psi, a tensile modulus of about 0.3 to 0.6 x 10^6 psi, a compressive strength of 14 to 20 x 10^3 psi and can elongate from 2 to 10%.
During curing the epoxy can shrink from 1 to 5%. Some of the epoxies used
for matrices, ERL 2772 (Union Carbide), DER 332 (Dow Chemical), and Epon
828 (Shell Chemical), are based on an uncured liquid with the molecular
structure

$$(CH_2 - CH - CH_2 - O - \langle \rangle -)_2 - C(CH_3)_2$$

They can be cured using **diethylenetriamine** ($H_2NCH_2CH_2NHCH_2CH_2NH_2$) with
the amine groups reacting with epoxy ($CH-CH_2$) groups to cross link the
molecules.

For higher temperature applications phenolics, polybenzimidazoles,
and polyimides have been used as matrices. A typical polyimide structure
has the formula

$$\left\{ N \begin{matrix} C \\ C \end{matrix} \langle \rangle \begin{matrix} C \\ C \end{matrix} N - \langle \rangle \right\}_n$$

and a typical polyimidazole has the formula

$$\left\{ C \begin{matrix} N \\ N \end{matrix} \langle \rangle \begin{matrix} N \\ N \end{matrix} C - \langle \rangle \right\}_n$$

Another high temperature resin, polybenzothiazole, is being studied
as a matrix for applications where good creep-rupture is important, and

other polymers such as bis-benzoinmidazophenantholine-dione are still
being developed.

ORGANIC MATRIX COMPOSITES

In the United States, most of the effort on high modulus composites
has been expended on boron fiber-epoxy matrix composites. Boron filament
can be made into a composite tape by drawing the fibers through an epoxy
resin, laying them side by side on a drum, and then cutting them off.
These tapes can then be joined together in various configurations.

Many of the properties of boron-epoxy composites have been well established. Data are given in Table 5.1. Tensile strengths of 220×10^3 psi
and moduli of 34×10^6 psi are quite common. Shear strengths of 14×10^3
psi are also obtained routinely and some values have been as high as 18×10^3 psi, but probably the most startling property of boron-epoxy composites
is the compressive strength which averages about 350×10^3 psi.

In England, researchers have concentrated on carbon-epoxy matrix
composites. To produce a typical composite, carbon tows or yarns are im-
mersed in epoxy in a suitable solvent and placed together. The resin and
hardner then can be poured over the wet fibers and spread. After the
"prepreg" is dried below the curing temperature, the single ply "prepregs"
can be pressed together. The properties of typical carbon fiber-epoxy
matrix composites are given in Table 5.1.

One of the largest problems with these carbon fiber reinforced composites has been their low shear strength. However, various gas and liquid
treatments have been used recently on the fibers to improve the carbon-epoxy
interface bonding. These improved shear strength values also are listed
in Table 5.1.

Another approach for improving the shear strength of carbon-epoxy
composites has been investigated by researchers at the Naval Ordinance

Table 5.1

PROPERTIES OF COMPOSITES

	Carbon-Epoxy	Boron-Epoxy	Borsic-Al	Borsic-Ti
Density (lbs/in^3)(g/cm^3)	0.056, 1.54	0.075, 2.1	0.1, 2.8	0.13, 3.6
Tensile Strength (10^3 psi)	130	225	190	175
Tensile Modulus (10^6 psi)	30	34	31	34
Specific Strength (10^6 in.)	2.3	3.0	1.9	1.3
Specific Modulus (10^6 in.)	530	450	310	260
Flexural Strength (10^3 psi)	104	260	220	
Flexural Modulus (10^6 psi)	24	40		
Shear Strength (10^3 psi)	2.5,7.5[a] 13[b],9.6[c]	14-18	15	
Shear Modulus (10^6 psi)			10	

Compressive Strength (10³ psi)		350	300	90
Compressive Modulus (10⁶ psi)		34	14	9
Transverse Strength (10³ psi)	40	12-15^e	12	
Transverse Modulus (10⁶ psi)			12	
Impact Strength (Charpy) (ft-lbs)		10		10
Poisson's Ratio		0.22		
Use Tem (°F)	700	600	450^d	450^d
Therm. Exp. Coeff. (10⁶/°C)		4^f,24g	3.3^f	-0.73^f
Erosion Resistance	Good	Good	Good	Poor

a – Thornel 50 fiber – treated,   b – Morganite II fiber – treated,   c – Morganite I fiber – treated,

d – Can be raised by using polyimide,   e – Can be increased to 40,000 psi by using titanium foil with plasma sprayed aluminum,   f – direction parallel to fibers axes,   g – perpendicular to fiber axes.

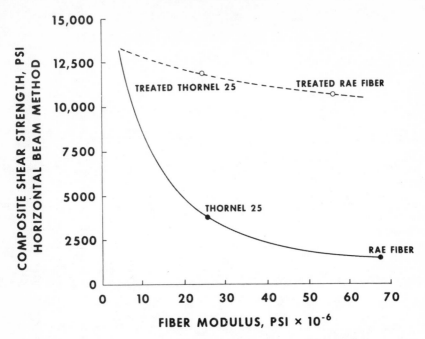

Fig. 5.1. Carbon fiber composite shear strength vs. fiber modulus, epoxy resin amine cure (after S. P. Prosen and K. Simon, <u>Reinforced Plastics and Composites World</u>, Sept./Oct. (1969).

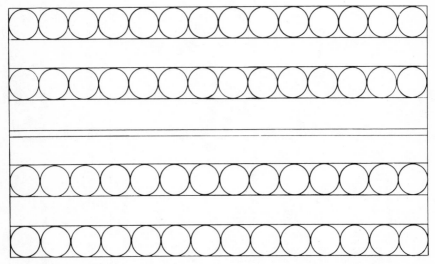

Fig. 5.2. Schematic of cross section of a balanced bidirectional composite specimen (0° orientation of outer plies) (after Materne and Kuhbander[1]).

Laboratory. They found that significant improvements could be attained by using silicon carbide whisker coated graphite fibers in the composites. This is shown in Fig. 5.1.

While the major effort on high modulus composites has involved boron and carbon fibers some studies have been conducted on silicon carbide-epoxy resin composites. Materne and Kubander[1] reported on the preparation and properties of some of these composites. The average tensile strength and modulus of the fibers used in the study was 360×10^3 psi and 61×10^6 psi respectively. These fibers were coated with Shell Chemical Company Epon 828 and Catalyst "Z" and wound on a mandrel to form a monolayer. The tapes then were joined together by pressing at 180°F and 30 psi for 1 hr and 350°F for 2 hours.

The average diameter of the filaments was 0.004 in. and the average density was 3.24 g/cm^3. For a composite containing 70 volume % filament, the density was 2.59 g/cm^3 and the shear strength 12.5×10^3 psi. A composite containing 62% filament had a tensile strength of 149,000 psi, a tensile modulus of 32.6×10^6 psi and a flexural strength and modulus of 260×10^3 psi and 33.4×10^6 psi respectively.

A series of balanced 8 ply bidirectional composites with the outer plies both oriented in the 0° direction (longitudinally) and the 90° direction (transverse) was prepared and tested. See Fig. 5.2. For a 65 fiber volume % composite, the composite density was 2.50 g/cm^3. The shear stress, flexural strength and modulus for the 0° direction test was 73×10^3 psi, 125×10^3 psi and 20.9×10^6 psi and for the 90° test was 55×10^3 psi, 84×10^3 psi and 11.2×10^6 psi respectively. The average compressive strength and modulus of a 63.1 volume % fiber composite was 161×10^3 psi and 25.9×10^6 psi.

The mechanical properties of these composites were improved by treating the surface of the fibers with either silane, thermal oxidation plus silane or pyrolyzed coating application plus silane. By these treatments, improvements of 30 to 45% in flexural strength were attained in bidirectional composites. The shear modulus was reported to be 2.4 x 10^6 psi.

H. S. Schwartz et al[2] have described work on some beryllium fiber-epoxy resin matrix composites. The beryllium fiber employed was 0.005 in. in diameter, had an ultimate tensile strength of about 160 x 10^3 psi and a modulus of about 36 x 10^6 psi. The composites were prepared with the fibers oriented in one, two and three directions. Rings were prepared to determine the unidirectional properties, while all the other composites were formed as flat laminates. The bidirection composites consisted of layers alternating at 0° and 90°, and tridirectional composites contained filaments rotated 60° in successive layers.

The density of a ring with 66 volume % fiber was 1.63 g/cm^3 and the ring had a tensile strength and modulus of 100 x 10^3 psi and 28 x 10^6 psi respectively. A bidirectional composite with beryllium fiber had a strength of 43.6 x 10^3 psi and a modulus of 9 x 10^6 psi. For a tridirectional composite with 10% less fiber, these values were 28 x 10^3 psi and 5.6 x 10^6 psi.

When 30 volume % of uniaxially oriented boron nitride fiber was placed in phenolics, a flexural strength of 23,300 psi and modulus of 1.33 x 10^6 psi was attained.[3] These values were 8000 psi and 0.6 x 10^6 psi, respectively, for the phenolics alone.

In a study of boron fiber-polyimide resin composites reported by Petker et al[4] the potential of this system at high temperature was demonstrated. To form the composites, the fiber was wound on a mandrel, impregnated with a polyimide and the "prepreg" sheets were cut off and pressed together at pressures between 1 and 100 psi at temperatures up to 400°F. These composites were then post cured at 600°F for two hours.

When the void content was kept below 2 volume %, the flexural and
interlaminar shear strength of the composites containing 27 to 33 wt %
resin was measured to be as high as 250×10^3 psi and 12×10^3 psi respectively. In addition, this study showed that a typical boron-polyimide
composite with a strength of approximately 190,000 psi retained 60 to 70%
of its strength at 500°F and 40% of its strength at 600°F.

High modulus carbon-polyimide composites have also been studied for
use at elevated temperatures. Copeland et al[5] in an early study showed
that shear strengths of nearly 2000 psi and flexural strengths of about
60×10^3 psi could be attained for Thornel 40-polyimide composites containing ∼ 60 volume % fiber.[2] In less than a year values of 5000 psi
and 130,000 psi for the shear and flexural strengths respectively have
been realized for these composites. At temperatures of 550°F, 40% of the
strength is retained after 1000 hrs.

One of the largest problems in attaining good properties with polyimide matrix composites is to achieve a low void content. This problem is
difficult due to the curing mechanism of the polyimide molecule, which
involves ring closure in the formation of the imide structure with the
loss of water. If this water can be removed from the composite, the properties will be improved as was demonstrated in the study by Petker et al.

METAL MATRIX COMPOSITES

A number of techniques have been employed to prepare high modulus
fiber metal composites. Harvey Aluminum[6] adapted its method of inserting
steel wires in an aluminum matrix to the formation of hot pressed boron
fiber reinforced aluminum composites. In this method, fibers of boron
are aligned between sheets of aluminum or aluminum alloys and hot pressed
under conditions selected to prevent fiber degradation. Using fiber
volume percentages of 45 to 50%, tensile strengths of 150,000 psi to

200,000 psi have been achieved. For beryllium fiber reinforced aluminum,
they attained ultimate tensile strength values of 100,000 psi.

TRW Systems[7] have used a similar method for preparing beryllium and
boron fiber reinforced aluminum. Some of their composites with 35 volume
% fiber had strengths of 123,000 psi for a boron fiber reinforced aluminum
composite and 78,000 psi for a beryllium reinforced aluminum composite and
moduli of 26 x 10^6 psi for the former composite and 21 x 10^6 psi for the
latter. To date the fatigue endurance limit of the Be-Al composites is
lower, the strength is much less, and the transverse elongation is less
than that of the B-Al composites. Beryllium reinforced titanium composites
have strengths of about 130,000 psi.

Workers at Solar also use a diffusion method for forming metal matrix
composites, but they employ grooved foils to improve the alignment of the
boron filaments in the composites. Other methods such as hot pressing,
liquid infiltration and electroforming have been investigated by General
Technologies Corporation. In addition to their work on B-Al and B-Mg
composites, they also have investigated silicon carbide fiber reinforced
aluminum, titanium and nickel matrices. Since silicon carbide is less
reactive than boron, these systems should be better than the boron reinforced metal matrices at elevated temperatures.

Boron-aluminum composites have also been prepared by plasma spraying
aluminum on boron fibers.[8,9] In this process, a metal foil is wrapped on
a drum, the filament is wound in a monolayer and the metal is then plasma
sprayed on the wire to form a foil. These foils are cut off the drum and
hot pressed together to form multilayer composites. Some degradation of
the fibers was observed mainly due to the hot pressing process. With care-
ful control of the process, composites were prepared with strengths of
approximately 170,000 psi. However, at elevated temperatures the boron
fibers react with the aluminum and the composites are degraded.[10]

Fig. 5.3. Plasma sprayed Borsic-aluminum composite fabricated from monolayer tapes (after K. Kreider and M. Marciano, <u>Trans. AIME</u>, <u>245</u>, 1279 (1969).

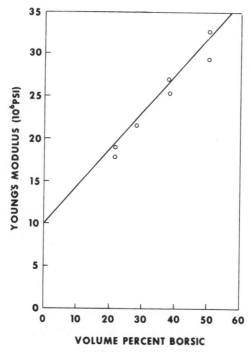

Fig. 5.4. Effect of fiber content on composite modulus (after K. Kreider and M. Marciano, <u>Trans. AIME</u>, <u>245</u>, 1279 (1969).

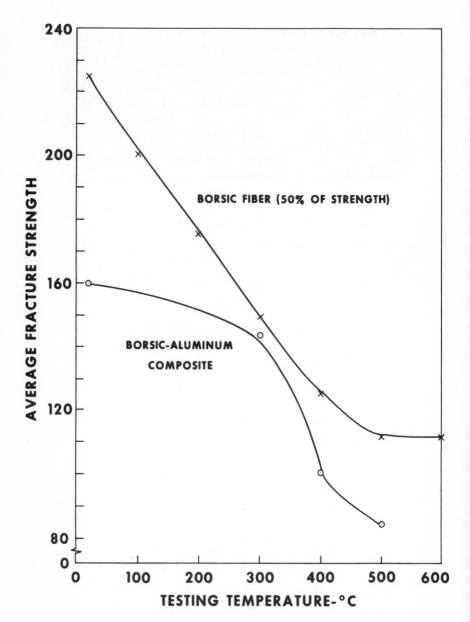

Fig. 5.5. Borsic-aluminum composite and Borsic fiber strength at temperature.

Table 5.2

PROPERTIES OF BORSIC-ALUMINUM COMPOSITES[*]

    The following properties are characteristic of composites of 50% Borsic (silicon carbide coated 0.004 inch boron fiber) and 50% by volume 6061 aluminum alloy matrix:

Density   = 2.7 grams/cc.
                                          (0.097 lb/in^3)

Elastic Properties
Young's Modulus (fiber direction)   = 30 x 10^6 psi
Young's Modulus (transverse direction) = 12 x 10^6 psi
Shear Modulus   = 7 x 10^6 psi
Poisson's Ratio   = 0.22 $\pm$ 0.01

Strength
Ultimate tensile strength (fiber direction) = 140 - 190,000 psi
Ultimate tensile strength   = 12 - 15,000 psi
   (transverse direction)
Interlaminar Shear Strength   = up to 13,000 psi

Creep-Stress Rupture -- 1000-hour fracture stress at 300°C is greater than 70,000 psi (fracture strain less than 2%).

Fatigue
Axial -- endures 10^6 cycles of 0 to 120,000 psi
Flexural -- endures 10^6 cycles of $\pm$ 100,000 psi

Impact -- Impact energy absorption is 2 1/2 ft-lbs on 1/2 size Charpy-notched impact specimen (approximately 10 times greater than a brittle material such as glass or beryllium).

PROPERTIES OF MULTIDIRECTIONAL BORSIC-ALUMINUM COMPOSITES

0°, $\pm$ 60° : 1000 hour fracture stress is 65,000 psi
0°, 90°   : 1000 hour fracture stress is 80,000 psi

[*]Data for composites made from Hamilton Standard, Division of United Aircraft Corporation, tape.

Silicon carbide fibers were employed in place of the boron fibers in some composites but the average strength of these fibers was not as high as that of boron fibers so that the strength of the composites was considerably lower. The most promising results were obtained with silicon carbide coated boron fibers (Borsic). No degradation of these fibers was observed after plasma spraying the aluminum on the fibers to produce the tapes and after hot pressing the tapes into composites. A photomicrograph of a polished cross section is shown in Fig. 5.3. The aluminum alloys used for the matrix were 1100 (pure aluminum), 6061 (Al + 1% Mg, 0.5% Si), 2024 (Al + 4.5% Cu), 390 (Al + 8% Si, 3% Cu) and 360 (Al + 9% Si). Of these, 6061 was selected as the best alloy, because it gave the best composite properties. The modulus of composites as a function of volume % fiber is given in Fig. 5.4. Other properties are listed in Table 5.2.

At high temperatures the strength of Borsic-aluminum composites is reduced. The strength of the composite decreases at higher temperatures in much the same way as the Borsic fiber alone. See Fig. 5.5. Above 300°C, the transverse strength of the composite is seriously reduced. In order to alleviate this problem, titanium foil has been used in place of aluminum. In some cases aluminum was plasma sprayed to form alternating aluminum and titanium layers in the composite and in others, titanium was plasma sprayed to produce an all titanium matrix. The technique of hot pressing of foils with Borsic fibers in between hot pressing Borsic fibers between foils also has been used to form titanium matrix composites.

APPLICATIONS

In determining the structures in which composites could be applied most effectively one should consider the properties given in Table 5.1. The high specific modulus of carbon-epoxy resin composites and the ease of bending the fine carbon fibers make this composite useful in structures where a light, stiff material is desired and the fibers can be used in structures where they have to be bent around a small radius. On the other hand, for applications which require high tensile, compressive and shear strengths boron-epoxy resin composites are more suitable. Where erosion or impact resistance is needed, boron-epoxy or preferably boron-aluminum or Borsic-aluminum composites offer a solution. For higher temperatures in structures requiring a better transverse strength, titanium or titanium-aluminum is a better matrix than aluminum.

Of course, in the early days of high modulus composites this information was not available, so that once the choice of the composite was made, problems that arose often were solved by designing around them.

In the United States, the Air Force made the decision to use boron-epoxy resin composites in aircraft structures, while in England the carbon-epoxy resin composites were being developed for engine blades. In both countries, composites were being considered for applications in which stiffness and weight savings were so important that the high cost of these new high modulus composites would not be a deterent to their use. It was felt that if the value of these composites could be proven, greater usage would follow, which in turn would lower the price and create new markets.

The experimental flights of a boron-epoxy resin horizontal tail section on a General Dynamics F-111 was a major step in moving composites into more general usage. Grumman provided the next step by designing and producing a wing box which is a more complex structure for use in either the FX fighter or the F-111.

Some of the secondary structures on aircraft which have been under study for some time are the wing tip for the F-111B, helicopter blades, floor beams for the 747, landing flaps for the A-4E, a main landing gear door for the F-5 and the outboard leading edge for the RA5C.

While this work was being conducted in the United States, Rolls-Royce was developing carbon-epoxy resin composite (Hyfil) compressor blades for their RB 211 turbofan engine. This engine, which is being made for use in Lockheed's 1011 air bus, will contain front-fan blades made of Hyfil. Since erosion of these blades is a problem, a thin coating of metal has been used to cover the composite material.

Where erosion or impact resistance is needed, some composite workers have preferred to use metal matrices. Marquardt and a team formed by General Dynamics' Convair Division and Harvey Aluminum are studying boron filament-reinforced aluminum for use as compressor blades.

For higher temperatures, plastics such as polyimides are being investigated as matrices for carbon and boron fibers. In another approach, Pratt and Whitney has used Borsic fibers in aluminum for fan blades in their JT8D engine. The silicon carbide coating on the boron fiber prevents fiber degradation during the fan blade fabrication process. This type of composite can be used at temperatures of 400° to 600°F. Silicon carbide-titanium and carbon-nickel composites have also been considered for this temperature range.

Developing composites for use at still higher temperatures presents a major challenge. Borsic-titanium, Borsic-nickel, silicon carbide-titanium, silicon carbide-nickel composites may be applicable at 700°F, but for higher temperatures new fibers are needed. Alumina fibers in high melting point matrices may be an answer to this problem in the future, but at present, controlled eutectic alloys offer the most promise for very high temperature applications.

EUTECTIC COMPOSITES

Another approach for obtaining high modulus composites is the unidirectional solidification of eutectic alloys. By this method a high

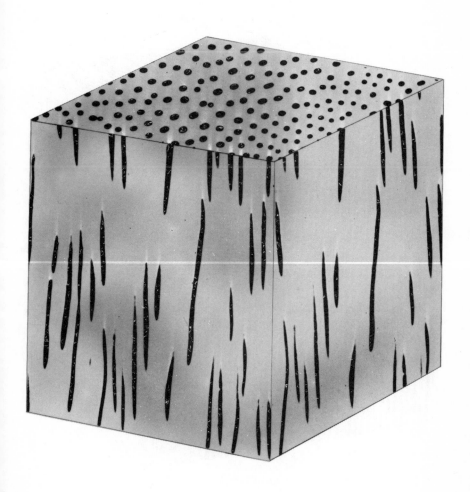

Fig. 5.6. Al-Al$_3$Ni controlled
eutectic.

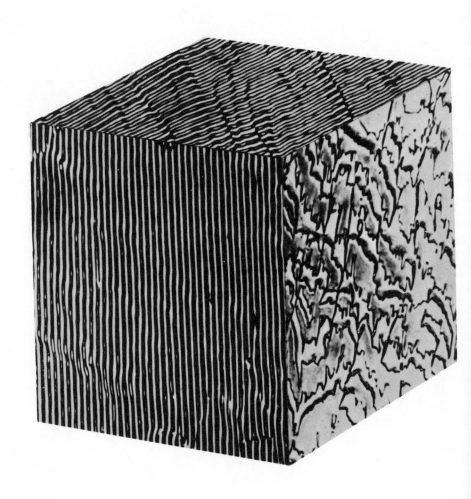

Fig. 5.7. Al-CuAl$_2$ controlled eutectic.

modulus phase can be grown in a ductile matrix in a single solidification process.   The unidirectional solidification can be accomplished by passing a molten zone along an ingot or slowly drawing the molten specimen from a furnace.   Two types of microstructures have been prevalent in these controlled specimens.   If the volumes of the two phases are nearly equal, the microstructure can consist of alternating parallel lamallae, while if the volume of one phase is significantly larger than that of the other, the microstructure can consist of rods of one phase imbedded in the other. See Fig. 5.6 and 5.7.

The controlled Al-Al$_3$Ni structure is a typical rod-like eutectic. The Al$_3$Ni rods are single crystals which grow so as to maintain a certain crystallographic relationship with the aluminum matrix.   In this system, the rods are faceted and definite crystallographic interfacial relationships exist between the two phases.[11]   It has been suggested that the two phases grow so that the interface between them is parallel to planes of nearly equal atomic density.   Thus, this microstructure should be stable and, indeed, high temperature studies have shown that the microstructure is retained at temperatures slightly below the melting point of the eutectic.[12]

As a consequence, not only is the strength of the unidirectionally solidified Al-Al$_3$Ni eutectic about three times that of the as cast material[13], (Fig. 5.8) but it also has considerable strength at elevated temperatures.   In composites which are "man made" (the fibers are placed in a matrix) there are often severe problems due to reaction of the fiber with the matrix at high temperatures.   Therefore, it is for high temperature applications that the eutectic type composites may be most useful.

The Al-Al$_3$Ni eutectic has a melting point of only 641°C, but its elevated temperature strength is higher than 7075-T6 which is a precipitation hardened aluminum alloy.   See Fig. 5.9.   A more promising system,

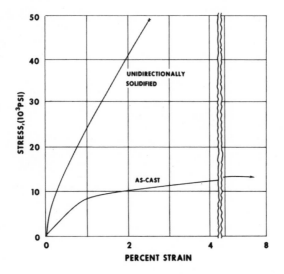

Fig. 5.8 Stress-strain curve for Al-Al$_3$Ni eutectic (after Salkind et al[16]).

because it contains a greater volume fraction of whiskers, 29% as opposed
to 11% for the Al-Al$_3$Ni system, and a higher melting point, is the Ta-Ta$_2$C
eutectic system.[14] The ultimate tensile strength of the controlled eutectic is 155,000 psi in comparison to 70,000 psi for the as received and
annealed material. See Fig. 5.10.

Another high temperature eutectic, Cb-Cb$_2$C, containing 31 volume %
whiskers was found to be better than all other columbium base alloys on
a specific strength basis.

In creep tests the Al-Al$_3$Ni eutectic exhibited a low minimum creep
rate, a short period of tertiary creep, and little rupture ductility.[15]
The creep resistance of this eutectic improves as the rate of solidification is increased. This is attributed to the fine, more closely spaced
whiskers in the rapidly grown eutectic which can effectively pin
dislocations.

The Al-Al$_3$Ni controlled eutectic also has shown good notch toughness.
Charpy impact tests have produced values from 8 to 30 ft-lbs depending on
the direction of the fibers. The high values were probably due to the
ductility of the aluminum matrix which acts as a good crack arresting
material.

Controlled eutectics such as Al-CuAl$_2$ with lamellar-type microstructures have also exhibited high strengths.[15] This composite contains 45
volume % CuAl$_2$ platelets and has a strength of 35,000 to 43,000 psi when
controlled and 12,000 psi for the as cast material. The higher temperature Ni-NiMo eutectic which also has a lamellar-type microstructure is
stronger at 2000°F than nickel superalloys.[17] It is felt that eutectics
such as this one, the Co-Co$_7$W$_6$ eutectic, and other nickel and cobalt based
eutectics will eventually be used for high temperature applications such
as gas turbine engine rotor blades and stator vanes.

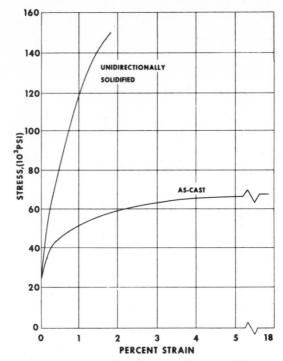

Fig. 5.9. Stress-strain curve for Ta-Ta$_2$C eutectic (after Salkind et al[16]).

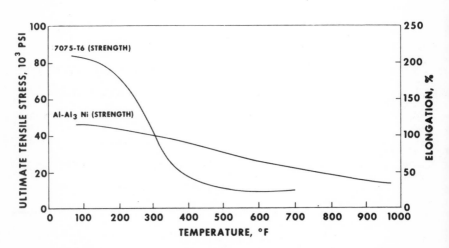

Fig. 5.10. Effect of temperature on the tensile strength of controlled Al-Al$_3$Ni eutectic (after Salkind et al[16]).

While the major emphasis on controlled eutectics has been structural in nature, considerable work of late has been conducted on eutectics for electrical, optical and magnetic applications. A review of these applications is presented in Ref. 18. In some of these cases, the improved strength of the material adds to its usefulness.

One of the earliest studies on eutectics for nonstructural applications in the United States was on the thermoelectric properties of an InSb-Sb controlled eutectic.[19] It was shown that the figure of merit for this system increased as the Sb rod size decreased. This study and one on the Bi_2Te_3-Te eutectic, demonstrated that anisotropic thermoelectric properties are achieved in controlled eutectics.

In Erlanger, West Germany, Weiss and Wilhelm reported the formation of a controlled NiSb-InSb eutectic[20], which contained conducting NiSb needles in an InSb matrix. This material can be used to polarize infrared light and it exhibits a large magnetoresistive effect. Some of the applications proposed for this material are a contact modulator for converting dc currents and potentials into ac potentials, a magnetically controlled resistor as a target emitter for the brake of German Federal Railway electric locomotives, and for direct control and operation of transistors such as those found in a collectorless dc motor.

In a recent study of the NaF-NaCl system, it was shown that the controlled specimen channeled light between the NaF rods to produce a "light pipe" effect.[21] In addition, the controlled eutectic is a far field infrared transmitting medium for wavelengths longer than the inter-rod distance (∽6 microns).

The magnetic properties of controlled eutectics are also interesting. It has been found from studies of the Fe-FeS and Fe_xSb-Sb eutectic systems that the coercive force of the controlled eutectic is increased by decreasing the diameter of the rods.[22,23] Other magnetic systems which have been investigated are the $Co-Y_2Co_{17}$, $Co-CoSb$, $Ni-Ni_3Sn$, and the $BaFe_{12}O_{19}^-$.$BaFe_2O_4$ eutectic.[18,24]

The $Cr-Cr_2O_3$ eutectic which contains highly conducting Cr rods in a Cr_2O_3 matrix has been considered for application requiring conduction paths through an insulating matrix and $Al-Al_3Ni$ has been suggested for use as a high strength conducting wire. These uses described above for controlled eutectics are only a few of those possible.

There are a large number of eutectics which have been studied (see Appendix I), but only a few have been evaluated for structural and non-structural applications. It is anticipated that some of these eutectics will be employed to solve the materials problems of the future.

REFERENCES

1. H. P. Materne, Jr. and R. J. Kuhbander, SAMPE, 10th National Meeting, San Diego, November (1966).

2. H. S. Schwartz, W. Mahieu and R. T. Schwartz, SAMPE, 10th National Meeting, San Diego, November (1966).

3. J. Economy, R. V. Anderson and D. T. Meloon, SAMPE, 10th National Meeting, San Diego, November (1966).

4. I. Petker, R. T. Sakakura and M. Segimoto, 23rd Ann. Techn. Conf. Society of the Plastics Industry, Inc., Washington, February (1968).

5. R. I. Copeland, D. R. Bealer and V. A. Chase, 23rd Ann. Techn. Conf. Society of the Plastics Industry, Inc., Washington, February (1968).

6. L. W. Davies, AIME Meeting, Cleveland, October (1967).

7. A. Toy, AIME Meeting, Cleveland, October (1967).

8. K. G. Kreider and G. R. Leverant, SAMPE, 10th National Meeting, San Diego, November (1966).

9. K. G. Kreider, AIME Meeting, Cleveland, October (1967).

10. M. Basche, R. Fanti and F. Galasso, Fibre Science and Technology, 1, 19 (1968).

11. W. K. Tice, W. R. Lasko and F. D. Lemkey, ASTM STP 430, 239 (1968).

12. B. Bayles, J. Ford and M. Salkind, Trans. AIME, 239, 844 (1967).

13. F. D. Lemkey, R. W. Hertzberg and J. A. Ford, Trans. AIME, 233, 334 (1965).

14. F. D. Lemkey and M. J. Salkind, Trans. AIME, 239, 844 (1967).

15. M. Salkind, F. Lemkey, F. George and B. J. Bayles, SAMPE, 10th National Meeting, San Diego, November (1966).

16. M. J. Salkind, F. D. George, F. D. Lemkey, B. J. Bayles and J. A. Ford, Chem. Eng. Progress, 62, 52 (1966).

17. E. R. Thompson and F. D. Lemkey, Materials Engineering, September (1968).

18. F. S. Galasso, J. of Metals, 19, 17 (1967).

19. W. K. Liebmann and E. A. Miller, J. Appl. Phys., 34, 2653 (1963).

20. H. Weiss and M. Wilhelm, Zeitschrift Fur Physik, 176, 399 (1963).

21. J. Batt, F. Douglas and F. Galasso, Cer. Soc. Bulletin, 48, 622 (1969).

22. D. L. Albright and R. W. Kraft, Trans. AIME, 236, 999 (1966).

23. F. Galasso, F. Douglas, W. Darby and J. Batt, J. Appl. Phys., 38, 3241, (1967).

24. F. Galasso, W. Darby, F. Douglas and J. Batt, J. Am. Cer. Soc., 50, 333 (1967).

APPENDIX

APPENDIX

A list of eutectics and data are presented. Under "Eutectics"
are listed elements involved and then the phases with the major component
in volume percent given last whenever it is known. In the next column
the structure and/or symmetry of the phases are given in the same order
as they are presented in the previous column. In the fourth column the
composition is given in wieght percent, atomic percent or mole percent
and sometimes also in volume percent, or in the case of complex inter-
metallics the number of rods which are found in a mm^2 of cross section.
The fifth column contains the eutectic melting point and the next column
contains the microstructure of the specimen. In the last column the
reference is given.

DATA FOR EUTECTICS

      Simple Eutectics

      Complex Oxides

      Complex Halides

      Organics

      Complex Intermetallics

TABLE 6.1. DATA FOR EUTECTICS

Simple Eutectics

Eutectic Elements	Phases	Structure and/or Symmetry	Composition	Eutectic Temp.(°C)	Microstructure	Ref.
Ag-Al	Ag_3Al_2-Al	hex. - F.C.C.	29.5 w/o Al	566	lamellar	1
Ag-Cu	Cu-Ag	F.C.C. - F.C.C.	39.9 a/o Cu, 74 v/o Ag	799	rod	2
Ag-Ge	Ge-Ag	D.C. - F.C.C.	81 w/o Ag	651	triang. dendritic	3
Ag-Pb	Ag-Pb	F.C.C. - F.C.C.	97.5 w/o Pb	304	normal	4
Ag-Sb	Ag_3Sb-Sb	orth. - hex.	56 w/o Ag	484	lamellar	3
Ag-Sn	Ag_3Sn-Sn	hex. - tetr.	96.5 w/o In	221		3
Al-B	AlB_2-Al	hex. - F.C.C.	.022 w/o B	660		5
Al-Ca	$CaAl_4$-Al	Dl_3 tetr. - F.C.C.	7.6 w/o Ca	616	$CaAl_4$ rods	5
Al-Co	Co_2Al_9-Al	monocl. - F.C.C.	2.3 v/o Co_2Al_9	657	Co_2Al_9 plates	2
				548	platelets	6
Al-Cu	$CuAl_2$-Al	B.C. tetr. - F.C.C.	82.7 m/o Al, 54 v/o Al	548	lamellar	7
Al-Fe	$FeAl_3$-Al	monocl. - F.C.C.	99.1 a/o Al, 3 v/o $FeAl_3$	655	$FeAl_3$ flakes	2
Al-Ge	Ge-Al	D.C. - F.C.C.	30.3 a/o Ge	424	dendrites; not controlled	2
Al-Mg	Mg-$Al_{12}Mg_{17}$	hex. - cubic	69.9 a/o Mg, 29 v/o Mg	437	lamellar	2
Al-Ni	Al_3Ni-Al	DO_2 orth. - F.C.C.	5.7 w/o Ni, 10 v/o Al_3Ni	640	rods of Al_3Ni; blades	8

System	Alloy	Structure	Temp.	Morphology	Ref.
Al-Pd	Al$_3$Pd-Al	orth. - F.C.C.	615	Chinese script	5
Al-Si	Si-Al	D.C. - F.C.C.	577.2	rods radiating	3
Al-Sn	Al-Sn	F.C.C. - tetr.	232	degenerate	5
Al-Th	Al$_3$Th-Al	hex. - F.C.C.	634	spiral	5
Al-Zn	Al-Zn	F.C.C. - hex.	382	lamellar	9
Au-Bi	Au$_2$Bi-Bi	F.C.C. - hex.	241	18 w/o Au — nonuniform	4
Au-Ge	Ge-Au	D.C. - F.C.C.	356	flake-like	2
Au-Pb	AuPb$_2$-Pb	B.C. tetr. - F.C.C.	215	lamellar	2
B-Fe	Fe-Fe$_2$B	B.C.C. - tetr.	1149	lamellar	5
B-Ni	Ni-Ni$_3$B	F.C.C. - orth.	1140	lamellar	10
B-Ti	TiB-Ti	orth. - hex.	1670	rod	11
Be-Co	CoBe-Co	CsCl / cubic - hex.	1120	lamellar	5
Be-Ni	NiBe-Ni	CaCl / cubic - F.C.C.	1157	lamellar	11
Bi-Cd	Bi-Cd	hex. - hex.	144	nonuniform	4
Bi-Mn	MnBi-Bi	NiAs / hex. - hex.	262	MnBi rods	5
Bi-Pb	Bi-Pb$_2$Bi	hex. - hex.	125	dendrites	3
Bi-Sn	Bi-Sn	hex. - tetr.	139	anomalous dendrites	3
Bi-Te	Bi$_2$Te$_3$-Te	hex. - hex.	413	Bi$_2$Te$_3$ plates	12

Composition notes (by system):
- Al-Pd: 24 w/o Pd
- Al-Si: 12.5% Si, 11 v/o Si
- Al-Sn: 99.5 w/o Sn
- Al-Th: 5 w/o Al
- Au-Bi: 18 w/o Au
- Au-Ge: 27 a/o Ge, 31 v/o Ge
- Au-Pb: 84.4 a/o Pb, 49 v/o AuPb$_2$
- B-Fe: 3.2 w/o B, 53 v/o Fe$_2$B
- B-Ni: 4 w/o B, 35 v/o Ni
- B-Ti: 3.3–3.6 w/o B, 17 v/o TiB
- Be-Co: 4 w/o Be, 23 v/o CoBe
- Be-Ni: 4.5 w/o Be, 38 v/o NiBe
- Bi-Cd: 60 w/o Bi
- Bi-Mn: .6 w/o Mn
- Bi-Pb: 56.5 w/o Bi
- Bi-Sn: 57 w/o Bi
- Bi-Te: 85 w/o Te, 27 v/o Bi$_2$Te$_3$

TABLE 6.1 (continued)

Eutectic Elements	Phases	Structure and/or Symmetry	Composition	Eutectic Temp.(°C)	Microstructure	Ref.
Bi-Zn	Zn-Bi	hex. – hex.	97.3 w/o Bi	254	uniform	4
C-Cr	$Cr_{23}C_6$-Cr	cubic – B.C.C.	3.5 w/o C	1500		5
C-Fe	Fe-Fe_3C	B.C.C. – hex.	4.3 w/o C, 59 v/o Fe_3C	1147	lamellar	13
C-Mo	Mo_2C-Mo	hex. – B.C.C.	1.8 w/o C	2200	acicular	5
C-Nb	Nb_2C-Nb	hex. – B.C.C.	1.5 w/o C, 31 v/o Nb_2C	2335	Nb_2C rods	14
C-Ta	Ta_2C-Ta	hex. – B.C.C.	.8 w/o C, 30 v/o Ta_2C	2800	Ta_2C rods	14
Cd-Pb	Cd-Pb	hex. – F.C.C.	82.6 w/o Pb	248	lamellar	15
Cd-Sb	CdSb-Cd	orth. – hex.	7 w/o Sb, 19 v/o CdSb	290	Chinese script not un. sol.	2
Cd-Sb	Sb-CdSb	hex. – orth.	57 a/o Sb, 13 v/o Sb	445	plate and rod	2
Cd-Sn	Cd-Sn	hex. – tetr.		177	rod very pure	4
Cd-Zn	Cd-Zn	hex. – hex.		266	rod very pure lamellar	15, 16
Co-Cr	CoCr-Co	tetr. – hex.	45 w/o Co	1470	dendrites	17
Co-Ge	$CoGe_2$-Co	orth. – hex.	29 w/o Ge, 33 v/o Co	1110	not controlled	5
Co-Mo	Mo_6Co_7-Co	$D8_5$ hex. – hex.	37% Co, 33 v/o Mo_6Co_7	1340	lamellar	17
Co-Nb	Co_2Nb-Co	cubic – hex.	39 v/o Co_2Nb	1235	lamellar	5
Co-S					rod type	5

Co-Sb	CoSb-Co	NiAs hex. - hex.	41 w/o Sb, 38 v/o Co	1113	lamellar	12
Co-Ta	$TaCo_2$-Co	cubic - hex.	29 w/o Ta, 35 v/o Co_2Ta	1980	rods & platelets	5
Co-W	W_6Co_7- Co		72.77 w/o W	1630	lamellar	12
Co-Y	Co-Y_2Co_{17}	hex.	9 w/o Y, 19 v/o Co	1340	rods	18
Cr-Cu	Cr-Cu	B.C.C. - F.C.C.	1.33% Cr, 2 v/o Cr	1083	Cr rods	5
Cr-Ni	Cr-(Ni^{SS}-Cr)	B.C.C. - F.C.C.	49 w/o Ni, 23 v/o Cr	1345	Cr rods & plates	19
Cr-O	Cr-Cr_2O_3	B.C.C. - hex.	20 w/o Cr, 15 v/o Cr	1660	rods	5
Cu-Mg	Mg_2Cu-Mg	orth. - hex.	30.7 w/o Cu	485	noncontrolled lamellar	
Cu-Nb	Nb-Cu rich	B.C.C. - F.C.C.	60 w/o Cu	1550	colony	5
Cu-O	Cu_2O-Cu	cubic - F.C.C.	.39 w/o O	1065	colony	5
Cu-P	Cu_3P-Cu	hex. - F.C.C.	8.4 w/o P	714	colony	
Cu-S	Cu_2S-Cu	orth. - F.C.C.	.77 w/o S	1065	colony	
Fe-Nb	Fe_2Nb-Fe	hex. - B.C.C.	17.8 w/o Nb, 35 v/o Fe_2Nb	1360	not controlled	
Fe-O	FeO-Fe	cubic - B.C.C.			FeO rods	
Fe-S	Fe-FeS	B.C.C. - NiAs hex.	31 w/o S, 9 v/o Fe	988	iron rods	20
Fe-Sb	Fe-Fe_xSb	B.C.C. - NiAs hex.	52 w/o Sb, 18 v/o Fe	1002	iron rods	21
Fe-Ti	Fe-TiFe	B.C.C. - cubic	14 w/o Ti	1340		5
Gd-Ni	Ni-$Ni_{15}Gd_2$	F.C.C. - hex.	92 w/o Ni, 52 v/o Ni	1290	Ni rods	12
In-Sn	In_3Sn-Sn	tetr. - tetr.	47.2 a/o Sn	117	lamellar & rods	2
In-Sb	Sb-InSb	ZnS / hex. - hex.	69 w/o Sb	530	triang. rods	22

TABLE 6.1 (continued)

Eutectic Elements	Phases	Structure and/or Symmetry	Composition	Eutectic Temp.(°C)	Microstructure	Ref.
Mg–Ni	Mg_2Ni–Mg	hex. – hex.	23.5 w/o Ni	507	short plates and rods	5
Mg–Sn	Mg_2Sn–Mg	CaF_2 cubic – hex.	36.4 w/o Sn, 76 v/o Mg	561	Chinese script rods or broken bars	23
Mg–Zn	Mg_2Zn_{11}–Zn	cubic – hex.	7.7 a/o Mg, 50 v/o Zn	367	spiral	2
Nb–Ni	Ni_3Nb–Ni	hex. – F.C.C.	23 w/o Nb, 26 v/o Ni_3Nb	1270	lamellar	2
Ni–Pb	Ni–Pb rich liquid	– F.C.C.			L_{II} in grain boundaries	5
Ni–S						
Ni–Sb	Ni–Ni_3Sb	F.C.C. – hex.	36 w/o Sb, 20 v/o Ni	1097	lamellar	12
Ni–Sn	Ni–Ni_3Sn	Mg_3Sn F.C.C. – hex.	32.5 w/o Sn, 38 v/o Ni	1130	Ni plates	12
Ni–Ta	$TaNi_3$–Ni	orth. – F.C.C.	37 w/o Ta, 13 v/o Ni_3Ta	1360	lamellar	5
Ni–Th	Ni–$Ni_{17}Th_2$	F.C.C. – hex.	79.5 w/o Ni, 48 v/o Ni	1300	Ni rods	5
Ni–Ti	Ni_3Ti–Ti	hex. – hex.	83 w/o Ni, 29 v/o Ni_3Ti	1287	acicular Ni	5
Ni–W	W–WNi_4	B.C.C. – tetr.	45 w/o W, 6 v/o W	1500	dendrites	5
Pb–Sb	Sb–Pb	hex. – F.C.C.	11.1 w/o Sb	251	lamellar	4
Pb–Sn	Pb–Sn	F.C.C. – tetr.	26.1 a/o Pb, 71.1 v/o Sn	183	lamellar	2
S–Sb	Sb–S rich L_{II}	monotectic			hex. array of liquid channels	5

Elements	Eutectic Phases A	B	Structure and/or Symmetry	Composition	Eutectic Temp.°C	Microstructure	Ref.
S-Sn	Sb-Sb$_2$S$_3$		hex. -			Sb rods & platelets	5
Si-V	Sn-SnS		tetr. - orth.			discont. plates	5
	V$_3$Si-V		-W / cubic -	7.5 w/o Si, 25 v/o V$_3$Si	1840		5
Sn-Zn	Zn-Sn		hex. - tetr.	91 w/o Sn	198	rod, lamellar	3,24
Th-Ti	Ti-Th		hex. - hex.	12 w/o Ti, 75 v/o Th	1190	rod	5

Complex Oxides

Ba-Fe-O	BaFe$_{12}$O$_{19}$-BaFe$_2$O$_4$		hex -	45 w/o BaO, 28.6 v/o A	1370	dendrite plates	25
K-Nb-O	KNbO$_3$-K$_3$NbO$_4$		pseudo cubic -		845	not controlled	5
Pb-Mo-O	PbMoO$_4$-PbO		tetr. -	65 m/o PbO	740	rods PbMoO$_4$	26
Pb-Nb-O	PbNb$_2$O$_6$ -		orth.	26.6 w/o PbO	1310	not controlled	5
	PbNb$_4$O$_{11}$						
Zn-NbO	ZnO-Zn$_3$Nb$_2$O$_8$		hex.		1300	not controlled	5

Complex Halides

Ca-Li-Na-F	NaF-CaF$_2$		NaCl CaF$_2$ / cubic - cubic	67 m/o A	810		26
Ca-Li-Na-F	CaF$_2$-NaF-LiF		cubic-cubic-cubic	10-37-54 m/o	850	plates	26
Li-Na-F	NaF-LiF		NaCl NaCl / cubic cubic	40 m/o A	652	plates	26

TABLE 6.1 (continued)

Elements	Eutectic Phases A B	Structure and/or Symmetry	Composition	Eutectic Temp.°C	Microstructure	Ref.
Mg-Na-F	NaF-MgF$_2$	NaCl rutile cubic - tetr.	77 m/o A	820	plates	26
Na-Pb-F	NaF-PbF$_2$	NaCl - cubic -	32 m/o A	540	rods	26
	LiF-NaCl	cubic - cubic			rods	27
	NaF-NaCl	cubic - cubic			rods	27
	NaF-NaBr	cubic - cubic			rods	27

Organics

Eutectic Phases A B	Structure	Composition	Eutectic Temp.°C	Microstructure	Ref.
acetanilide - lactophenin		53.0 w/o B	83		28
anesthesin - acetanilide		33.0 w/o B	69		28
azobenzol - trional		52.0 w/o B	48		28
benzil - lactophenin		25.5 w/o B	86		28
$C_{12}H_{10}N_2$-$C_8H_6O_3$		26.0 w/o B	26	lamellar	29
$C_{10}H_{16}O$-$C_{10}H_8$		41.0 w/o B	30	plate-like	29
$C_{10}H_{16}O$-$C_6H_5CO_2H$		39.0 w/o B	60		29
$C_{10}H_{16}O$-$(CH_3CO_2)_2C_6H_4$		27.0 w/o B	40	rod-like	29

Complex Intermetallics

	Structure	Composition / Density	Temp.	Morphology	
CrAs–GeAs	MnP ZnS, orth. – cubic	35.4 w/o A		rods & lamellar	30
MoAs–GeAs	MnP ZnS, orth. – cubic	9.4 w/o A			30
VAs–GaAs	MnP ZnS, orth. – cubic	8.4 w/o A		rods & lamellar	30
CrAs–InAs	MnP ZnS, orth. – cubic	1.7 w/o A, $0.8 \times 10^4/\text{mm}^2$	937	rods	30
FeAs–InAs	MnP ZnS, orth. – cubic	10.5 w/o A, $2.5 \times 10^4/\text{mm}^2$		rods	30
$CoGa_{1.3}$ – GaSb	CsCl ZnS, cubic – cubic	7.9 w/o A, $17.0 \times 10^4/\text{mm}^2$	697	rods	30
CrSb–GaSb	NiAs ZnS, hex. – cubic	13.4 w/o A, $5.2 \times 10^4/\text{mm}^2$	690	rods	30
$FeGa_{1.3}$ – GaSb	ZnS, tetr. – cubic	7.9 w/o A, $3.3 \times 10^4/\text{mm}^2$	695	rods	30
GaV_3Sb_3–GaSb	– ZnS, cubic	0.49 w/o A	710		30
V_2Ga_5–GaSb	ZnS, tetr. – cubic	4.4 w/o A	707		30
CrSb–InSb	NiAs ZnS, hex. – cubic	0.6 w/o A, $0.6 \times 10^4/\text{mm}^2$	516	rods	30

TABLE 6.1 (continued)

Eutectic Phases	Structure	Composition	Eutectic Temp.°C	Microstructure	Ref.
FeSb-InSb	NiAs ZnS hex. - cubic	0.67 w/o A, $2.2 \times 10^4/\mathrm{mm}^2$	520	rods	30
Mg_3Sb_2-InSb	A-rare earth ZnS cubic hex. -	2.2 w/o A	519	lamellar	30
MnSb-InSb	NiAs ZnS hex. - cubic	6.5 w/o A, $8.1 \times 10^4/\mathrm{mm}^2$	510	rods	30
NiSb-InSb	NiAs ZnS hex. - cubic	1.8 w/o A, $8.2 \times 10^4/\mathrm{mm}^2$	517	rods	30

Appendix   **111**

REFERENCES

1. E. C. Elwood and K. Q. Bagley, J. Inst. Met., 76, 631 (1949).

2. R. W. Kraft, F. D. Lemkey, D. L. Albright, and F. D. George, UAR A-110069-5, August (1962).

3. L. F. Mondolfo, J. of Australian Inst. of Metals, 10, 169 (1965).

4. C. W. Haworth and E. P. Whelan, J. of Australian Inst. of Metals, 10, 184 (1965).

5. Prepared at United Aircraft Research Laboratories.

6. V. deL. Davies, J. of Inst. of Metals, 10, 93 (1964-65).

7. R. W. Kraft, Trans. AIME, 221, 95 (1961).

8. F. D. Lemkey, R. W. Hertzberg and J. A. Ford, Trans. AIME, 233, 334 (1965).

9. M. G. Day and A. Hellawell, J. Australian Inst. of Metals, 9, 213 (1964).

10. S. Shapiro, M.S. Dissertation, Rensselaer Polytechnic Institute (1964).

11. F. D. Lemkey, B. J. Bayles and M. J. Salkind, Final Report UACRL D910261-4, Contract Da-19-020-AMC-00434(X), July 31 (1965).

12. F. Galasso, J. of Met., 19, 17 (1967).

13. M. P. Wilkenson and A. Hellawell, British Cast. Iron Res. Assoc. J., 11, 439 (1963).

14. F. D. Lemkey and M. J. Salkind, International Conference for Crystal Growth, Boston, June (1966).

15. J. D. Hunt and J. P. Chilton, J. of Inst. of Metals, 91, 338 (1962-63).

16. A. W. Straumanis and N. Brakss, Z. Phys. Chem. 30B, 117 (1935).

17. R. L. Ashbrook and J. F. Wallace, Trans. AIME, 236, 670 (1966).

18. F. D. Lemkey and R. W. Kraft, Rev. Sci. Instr., 33, 846 (1962).

19. C. Hulse, United Aircraft Research Laboratories, Private communication.

20. D. L. Albright and R. W. Kraft, Trans. AIME, 236, 998 (1966).

21. F. Galasso, F. Douglas, W. Darby, and J. Batt, J. Appl. Phys., 38, 3241 (1967).

22. W. K. Liebmann and E. A. Miller, J. Appl. Phys., 34, 2653 (1963).

23.   R. W. Kraft, F. D. Lemkey and F. D. George, UAR A-110069-3
      June (1962).

24.   A. W. Straumanis and N. Brakss, Z. Phys. Chem. 38B, 140 (1937).

25.   F. Galasso, W. Darby, F. Douglas, and J. Batt, J. Am. Cer. Soc.,
      50, 333 (1967).

26.   M. Nichols and W. Lasko, United Aircraft Research Laboratories,
      Patent Pending (1963).

27.   S. G. Loxham and A. Hellawell, J. Am. Chem. Soc., 47, 184 (1964).

28.   A. Kolfert, J. of Australian Inst. of Metals, 10, 132 (1965).

29.   F. D. Lemkey, United Aircraft Research Laboratories, U. S. Patent
      Pending (1963).

30.   A. Muller and M. Wilhelm, Int. Conf. on Crystal Growth, Boston,
      June (1966).

INDEX

INDEX

Aluminum fibers, 9
Aluminum-copper aluminum eutectic, 90
Aluminum-nickel aluminide eutectic, 88, 90
Aluminum oxide fibers, 14, 59, 67
Aluminum oxide whiskers, 11
Antimony-indium antimonide eutectic, 91

$BaFe_{12}O_{19}$-$BaFe_2O_4$ eutectic, 92
Beryllium fibers, 7, 16, 59
Beryllium oxide whiskers, 12
Beryllium-reinforced epoxy composites, 78
Beryllium-reinforced titanium composites, 80
Boron-reinforced aluminum composites, 80
Boron carbide fibers, 16, 59, 66
Boron fibers, 9, 12, 19
Boron nitride fibers, 16, 59, 65
Boron reactor, 21
Boron-reinforced aluminum composites, 79
Boron-reinforced epoxy composites, 73
Boron-reinforced magnesium composites, 80
Boron-reinforced polyimide composites, 78
Borsic fibers, 14, 34
Borsic-reinforced aluminum composites, 84
Borsic-reinforced titanium composites, 84

Carbon fibers, 13, 41
Carbon-reinforced polyimide composites, 79
Carbon-reinforced resin composites, 73
Carbon whiskers, 12
Chromium fibers, 9
Coated boron fibers, 34

Organic matrices, 71
Organic matrix composites, 73, 78, 79
Oxide fibers, 14, 59, 67

Phenol matrix, 72
Polyacrylonitrile fibers, 13, 43, 44, 49, 52, 55, 56
Polyimide-boron composites, 78
Polyimide-carbon composites, 79

Rayon fibers, 13, 44

S glass, 6
Sapphire wiskers, 9
Silica fibers, 6
Silicon carbon fibers, 14, 59
Silicon carbide-reinforced aluminum composites, 80
Silicon carbide-reinforced nickel composites, 80
Silicon carbide-reinforced titanium composites, 80
Silicon carbide whiskers, 11
Silicon nitride whiskers, 11
Sodium fluoride-sodium chloride eutectic, 91
Stainless steel fibers, 10
Steel-reinforced aluminum composites, 79

Tantalum fibers, 8
Tantalum-tantalum carbide eutectic, 90
Taylor process, 7
Tellurium-bismuth telluride eutectic, 91
Titanium boride fiber, 16, 59, 67
Titanium wire, 10
Tungsten borides, 26
Tungsten fibers, 10
Tungsten oxide whiskers, 12

Unidirectional solidification, 6, 88

Whisker, 11, 12

Zircon fiber, 68
Zirconia fibers, 14, 59